GRADE 4

Practice Book

B

The McGraw·Hill Companies

Published by Macmillan/McGraw-Hill, of McGraw-Hill Education, a division of The McGraw-Hill Companies, Inc., Two Penn Plaza, New York, New York 10121.

Printed in the United States of America

11 12 13 PRS 15 14 13

Contents

Unit 1 • Growing Up

Contents

Unit 2 • Making a Difference

Contents

Unit 3 • The Power of Words

Contents

Unit 4 • Working Together

Contents

Unit 5 • Habitats

Contents

Unit 6 • Problem Solving

Name ______________________________

endless	display	protested
sensible	paralyzed	realistic

A. Replace the underlined word(s) with one of the words from the vocabulary list.

1. I complained about traveling alone. ____________

2. A trip in space may seem without a finish. ____________

3. The film about space travel was the way things are. ____________

4. His plan for launching a rocket was not well thought-out.

____

5. The astronaut seemed unable to move when he climbed outside the spaceship. ____________

B. Use three of the vocabulary words in sentences of your own.

6. ______________________________

____

7. ______________________________

____

8. ______________________________

____

Name ______________________________

Understanding the **characters** and the **setting** can help you understand the **plot development**—what happens in a story.

Read the passage. Then answer the questions that follow.

When she was little, Andrea lived near the Kennedy Space Center. Her mother always took her there to watch the rockets launch. As Andrea grew up, she realized that she wanted to do more than just watch rocket launches. More than anything, she wanted to be an astronaut, but she wasn't sure that she could be one.

Her mother told her, "If you want something, the important thing is that you try your best." Andrea ate well and exercised. She studied hard in all her subjects. After college she learned to fly jet planes.

Andrea's dream came true. She became an astronaut and took many trips into space.

1. Who are the characters in this story?

____

2. What is the setting when Andrea is a little girl?

____

3. How did Andrea's mother help her achieve her goal?

____

4. In most plots, a character changes. How did Andrea change in the story?

____

____

____

Name ______________________________

As you read *The Astronaut and the Onion,* fill in the Character Web.

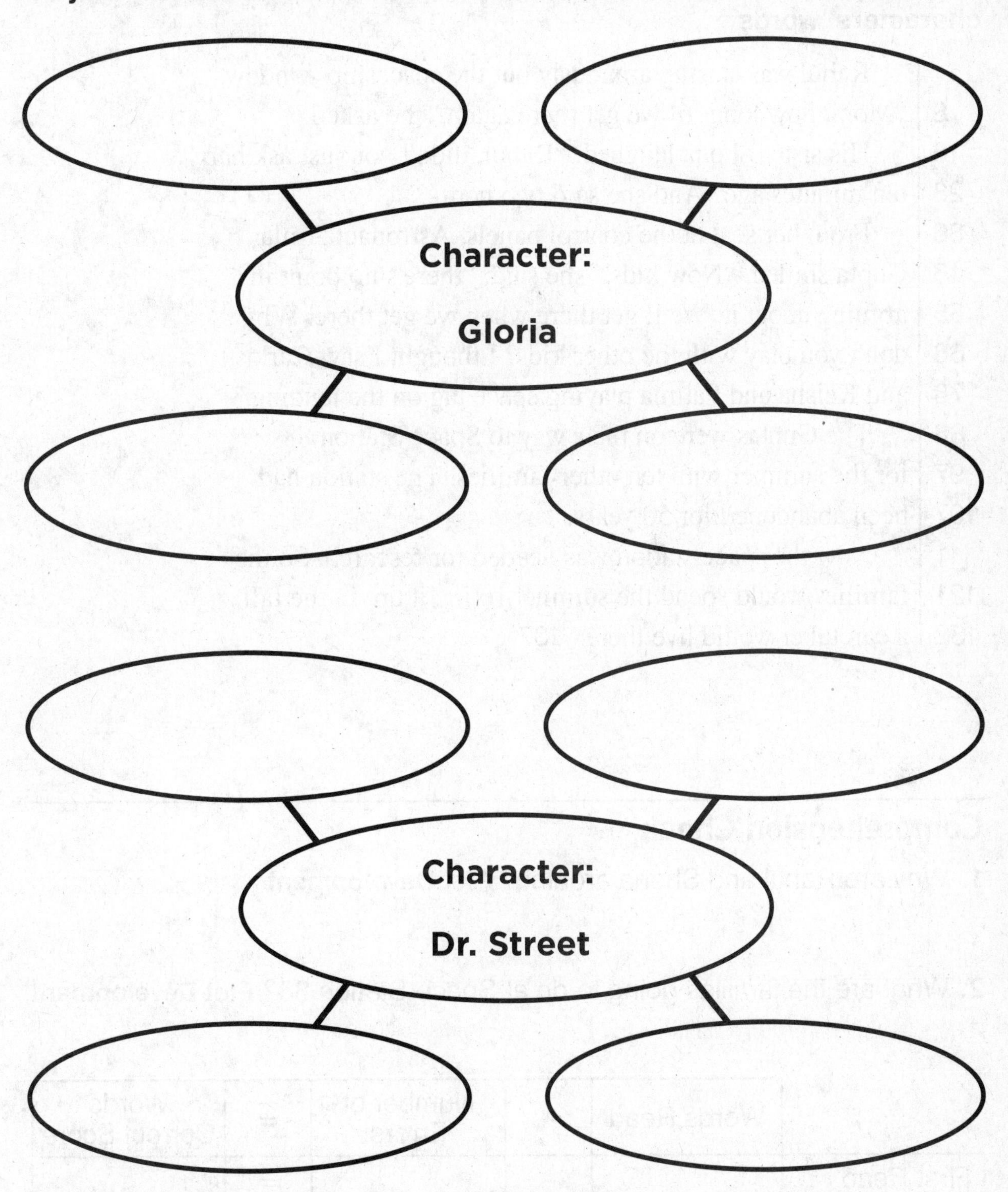

How does the information you wrote in the Character Web help you analyze and make inferences about *The Astronaut and the Onion*?

Name ______________________________

As I read, I will pay attention to pauses, stops, intonation, and characters' words.

	Rahul was staring anxiously out the spaceship window.
8	"Mom, how long 'til we get there again?" he asked.
18	His sister Shona laughed. "Rahul, didn't you just ask her
28	ten minutes ago? And she said two hours?"
36	From her seat at the control panels, Astronaut Amla
45	Gupta smiled. "Now kids," she said, "there's no point in
55	arguing about it. We'll get there when we get there. Why
66	don't you play with the other kids? I thought I saw Carlos
78	and Keisha and Fatima playing space tag on the landing."
88	The Guptas were on their way to Space Station 88
97	for the summer with ten other families. The station had
107	been abandoned for 50 years.
111	Now the space station was needed for research. So the
121	families would spend the summer fixing it up. In the fall,
132	a caretaker would live there. 137

Comprehension Check

1. Why are Rahul and Shona arguing? **Plot Development**

2. What are the families going to do at Space Station 88? **Plot Development**

	Words Read	–	Number of Errors	=	Words Correct Score
First Read		–		=	
Second Read		–		=	

CA **R 1.1** Read narrative and expository text aloud with grade-appropriate fluency and accuracy and with appropriate pacing, intonation, and expression.

Name ______________________________

A **metaphor** compares two different objects or ideas and states that one is the other. For example, *The farmer is a magician who makes vegetables pop out of the soil.*
Personification is a literary device in which animals or things are given human characteristics.

Read the following poem. Then answer the questions that follow.

The Road Worker

The worker wrestles with his jackhammer
As it stomps its mighty foot
Breaking and bruising the road.
Then the worker covers the road
With a soothing, warm, black blanket.
"Ah!" sighs the road.

1. What is an example of personification in this poem?

____

2. What is another example of personification in the poem?

____

3. To what does the poet compare road tar?

____

4. On the lines below, write a metaphor about one of the following:

firefighter doctor trash collector teacher artist

____

____

CA **R 3.5** Define figurative language (e.g., simile, metaphor, hyperbole, personification) and identify its use in literary works.

Name ______________________________

When you are reading and come to a word you do not know, a dictionary can tell you what the word means and how to say it.

dis•tort (di stôrt´) *verb.* **1.** to twist the meaning of something. *The reporter* distorts *what people say.* **2.** to twist out of shape. *The mirror* distorts *my face when I look into it.*

A phonetic spelling tells you how to say the word. Notice that *distort* is divided into two parts. Each part is called a **syllable**.

The accent mark (´) after the second syllable shows you which syllable to stress when pronouncing the word.

Use the dictionary entry above to answer these questions.

1. Which meaning of *distort* do you find in the following sentence?

Eduardo twisted the hanger and distorted its shape.

a. Meaning #1 **b.** Meaning #2

2. True or false: *distort* has two syllables.

a. true **b.** false

3. Which is the correct way to say *distort*?

a. di´ stôrt **b.** di stôrt´

4. Use *distort* in a sentence of your own. Then write the number of the meaning you used.

____

____

I used meaning # ____.

Name ______________________

Using the Word Study Steps

1. LOOK at the word.
2. SAY the word aloud.
3. STUDY the letters in the word.
4. WRITE the word.
5. CHECK the word.
Did you spell the word right?
If not, go back to step 1.

Silly Questions

Use the words in the box to complete the riddles.

drive	pride	slight	fright	spy
file	pry	climb	inside	minding
kite	shy	sly	pies	twice
wipe	prime	sigh	die	height

1. If I go ______________ out, can I go outside in?
2. If the sun were ______________, would it try to hide?
3. When I grow wings, can I fly as high as a ______________?
4. If the ladder reaches high enough, can I ______________ to the sky?
5. If I don't look all right, will I look like a ______________?
6. I am never early, but can I take ______________ in always being late?
7. If my onion begins to cry, will I give a ______________?
8. If Juan has mud, can he make ______________?
9. If I'm ______________ my business, will someone take care of me?
10. If my book could ______________, what stories would it tell about me?
11. If I walk one hundred miles, should I ______________ one half a mile?
12. If a sad song makes a tulip cry, will the tulip ______________?
13. If I try to hammer the bottle open, can I ______________ the bottle closed?
14. If a mouse has great ______________, is it a giant short?
15. If one is ______________, is two once?

CA **LC 1.7** Spell correctly roots, inflections, suffixes and prefixes, and syllable constructions.

Name ______________________________

A. There are six spelling mistakes in this fantasy story of traveling to the sun. Circle the misspelled words. Write the words correctly on the lines below.

Long, long ago, a girl named Annabelle wanted to go to the sun. She could not clime there because there were no ladders high enough. She rode her horse for three days until she reached a mountain of great hite. There she asked Bird-of-All-Birds if he had ever flown to the sun. "Yes," he said. "I take great pryde in my trip." Annabelle heard him sye. "It is a difficult trip," he said. "Will you take me there?" asked Annabelle. Bird-of-All-Birds flapped his wings twiece and off they flew. They came to a golden land. Annabelle was so excited she had to wiep the tears from her eyes. "Bird-of-All-Birds," she asked, "are there other places we can visit in the sky?" The great bird took her to the moon, and then to other wonderful lands. They spent their lives exploring.

1. ______________ 3. ______________ 5. ______________

2. ______________ 4. ______________ 6. ______________

B. Writing Activity

Write an advertisement for riding a spaceship to visit one of our planets. Use at least four spelling words.

____

____

____

____

____

____

____

CA **LC 1.7** Spell correctly roots, inflections, suffixes and prefixes, and syllable constructions.

Name ______________________________

- A sentence that contains two related ideas joined by a conjunction other than *and*, *but*, or *or* is called a **complex sentence**.

To form a complex sentence, combine these ideas using the given conjunction. Be sure that the new sentence makes sense.

1. The astronaut eats his meal. He floats around in the rocket. (as)

____

____

2. Light leaves a star. It takes thousands of years to reach Earth. (after)

____

____

3. Eat some freeze-dried snacks. You work at the computer. (while)

____

____

4. He goes to the library. He reads books about space. (where)

____

5. Mom doesn't want me to come along. It is dangerous. (since)

____

6. Fasten your seatbelts. The ship takes off. (before)

____

7. He brought a chunk of moon rock. He came home for the holidays. (when)

____

____

8. They watched. The rocket blasted off into space. (as)

____

CA **LC 1.2** Combine short, related sentences with appositives, participial phrases, adjectives, adverbs, and prepositional phrases.

Name ______________________________

- Remember that some conjunctions tell *where*, *when*, *why*, *how*, or *under what condition*.

Rewrite the letter below. Fix any spelling, punctuation, and grammar mistakes.

678 Saturn Road
Baltimore MD 21204
July 11 2007

Mr. and mrs. Rhodes
39 Sunshine drive
Baltimore MD 21286

dear Mr. and Mrs. Rhodes

I would like to be an astronaut. Because it would be exciting. You were the first people to travel to Mars. I bet you know a lot about space travel. I would like to learn more about outer space? I want to travel to mars someday. I also plan to visit Jupiter and Venus. Do you know which schools I could go to!

sincerely
Diana Smith

____

____

____

____

____

____

____

____

CA LC 1.0 Written and Oral English Language Conventions
LC 1.1 Use simple and compound sentences in writing and speaking.

Name ______________________________

1. Choose a single object in the room.

2. Write 3 sentences about that one object alone.

Example: The old map hangs crookedly on the bulletin board behind Ms. Andrews' desk. It's faded and worn and the top right corner is folded over like a floppy dog's ear. Its edges are stained brown and yellow, and it smells like old library books.

Extra Practice: Choose another single object in the room and do this exercise again.

____

____

____

____

____

____

____

____

____

____

____

____

____

____

Name ______________________________

The long **o** sound can be spelled several different ways.
stole (o_e) foam (oa) flow (ow) mold (o)

Fill in the blanks using each long *o* word in the box once.

boat	close	floating	shallow	know
most	don't	home	soaked	go
rowed	owned	Cole	foal	hoped

1. We were ______________ in our ______________.
2. Along the bank we saw the ______________ beautiful white horse.
3. I asked ______________ if he knew who ______________ her.
4. He answered, "I ______________ ______________."
5. Just then I caught sight of something small and brown and whispered,
   "She has a ______________!"
6. "How ______________ do you think we can get?" I asked.
7. I ______________ to feed them the leftover apples from our lunch.
8. We ______________ until the bottom scuffed against something below us and I stepped out to wade through the
   ______________ water to shore.
9. To my surprise I promptly sank instead. I got ______________! Cole thought it was hysterical!
10. "Let's ______________ ______________," I grumbled.

Name ______________________________

aware	selecting	positive	consisted	peculiar	advanced

A. Complete each sentence with a word from the box.

1. As the sound grew louder, Connie became ____________ that a train was coming.
2. Ted had trouble ____________ a different book because he liked to read only mysteries.
3. "You have a ____________ taste in music," Tobie told Andre. "I never thought I would meet a nine-year-old who liked Bach."
4. Andre's choices at the library always ____________ of history books about the period too.
5. "I am absolutely ____________ that you will love this book about horses," Laura assured Marie.
6. Both girls then argued over which of the two was the more ____________ reader.

B. Write a sentence using the word listed.

7. peculiar ______________________________

____

8. selecting ______________________________

____

C. Write a definition of the listed word, using your own words.

9. advanced ______________________________

The order in which events happen in a story is the **sequence**, or chronological order. To list events in chronological order, look for key words like first, then, and last.

Read the passage below. Then answer the questions that follow.

It was our town's worst storm. The next morning we saw our library had been struck by lightning and then caught fire. After seeing my favorite building in ruins, I decided something needed to be done.

First, I wrote a letter to our town's mayor. I emphasized the importance of having a library and why we needed to rebuild. Then, I decided to raise money. I asked some friends to help. Together, we baked cupcakes, washed cars, and collected money. I even got people to sign a petition—a piece of paper asking for something—saying that we needed to build a new library.

Finally, I took all the money we had raised along with the petition to the mayor's office. It turned out that the mayor had already been busy trying to design a new library. He was really impressed with all the work I had done and asked me to continue raising money for the new library!

1. What was the first thing that happened to the public library? How do you know? ______________________

____

2. What was the first thing the narrator did? What was the second thing?

____

____

3. What was the last thing the narrator did for the library? ______________________

____

____

CA **R 2.1** Identify structural patterns found in informational text (e.g., compare and contrast, cause and effect, sequential or chronological order, proposition and support) to strengthen comprehension.

As you read *Because of Winn-Dixie*, fill in the Sequence Chart.

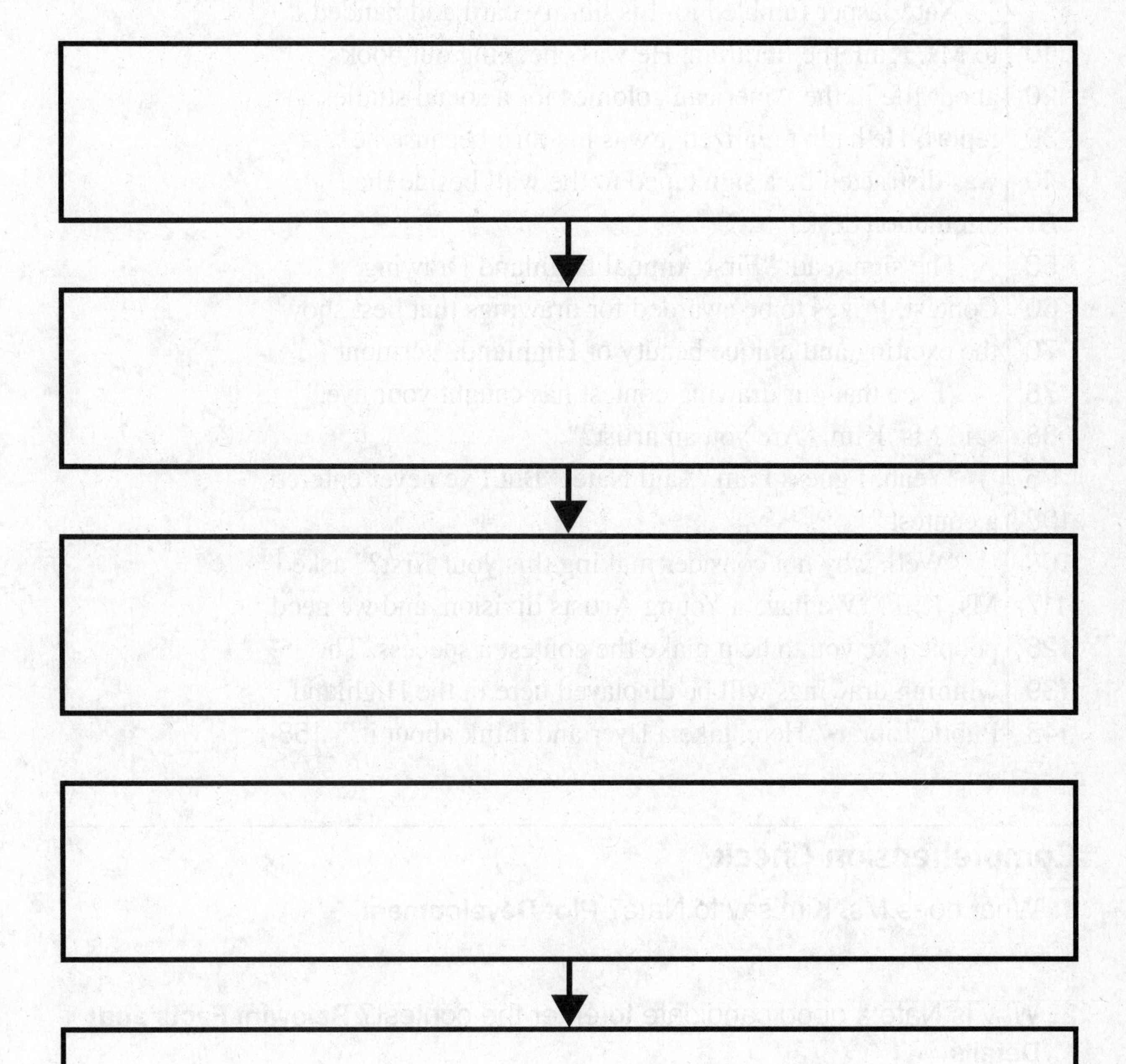

How does the information you wrote in the Sequence Chart help you to evaluate *Because of Winn-Dixie*?

Name ______________________________

Practice

Fluency: Intonation and Pacing

As I read, I will pay attention to end punctuation.

	Nate Jasper fumbled for his library card and handed it
10	to Ms. Kim, the librarian. He was checking out books
20	about life in the American colonies for a social studies
30	report. He hadn't realized it was his turn because he
40	was distracted by a sign taped to the wall beside the
51	circulation desk.
53	The sign read: "First Annual Highland Drawing
60	Contest. Prizes to be awarded for drawings that best show
70	the exciting and unique beauty of Highland, Vermont."
78	"I see that our drawing contest has caught your eye,"
88	said Ms. Kim. "Are you an artist?"
95	"Yeah, I guess I am," said Nate. "But I've never entered
106	a contest."
108	"Well, why not consider making this your first?" asked
117	Ms. Kim. "We have a Young Artists division, and we need
128	people like you to help make the contest a success. The
139	winning drawings will be displayed here in the Highland
148	Public Library. Here, take a flyer and think about it." 158

Comprehension Check

1. What does Ms. Kim say to Nate? **Plot Development**

2. Why is Nate a good candidate to enter the contest? **Relevant Facts and Details**

	Words Read	–	Number of Errors	=	Words Correct Score
First Read		–		=	
Second Read		–		=	

R 1.1 Read narrative and expository text aloud with grade-appropriate fluency and accuracy and with appropriate pacing, intonation, and expression.

Name ____________________

Onomatopoeia is the use of a word to imitate a sound.
A **simile** compares two different things using *like* or *as.*

Read the poem below. Then answer the questions that follow.

Books

What can you do with books, anyway?
You can laugh at them,
frown at them, slam them shut.
You can stack them cover to cover
till they're as tall as a skyscraper.
You can stuff them in your backpack
till it's heavy like an elephant.
Or you can take one, crack it open,
and read.

1. Which word in the third line of the poem is an example of onomatopoeia?

____

2. Write the two similes that appear in the poem.

____

____

3. What two things are being compared in the similes you wrote above?

____

____

4. Why is the poet's use of the word *slam* an example of onomatopoeia?

____

____

CA **R 3.5** Define figurative language (e.g., **simile**, metaphor, hyperbole, personification) and identify its use in literary works.

Name ____________________

The dictionary definition of a word is its **denotation.**
The feelings associated with a word are its **connotation.**

The bold words in each pair of sentences below have similar denotations, but their connotations are different. Write the feelings you associate with each word.

1. The day was **crisp**—just perfect for taking a walk.

____

2. The day was **raw**. How I wish I'd worn my gloves.

____

3. Alicia is really **goofy.**

____

4. Alicia is really **funny.**

____

5. Juan was **thrifty** and saved his money.

____

6. Juan was **cheap** and spent hardly any of his money.

____

Name ______________________________

Using the Word Study Steps

1. LOOK at the word.
2. SAY the word aloud.
3. STUDY the letters in the word.
4. WRITE the word.
5. CHECK the word.
   Did you spell the word right?
   If not, go back to step 1.

Find and Circle

Where are the spelling words?

C	H	O	S	E	R	M	A	S	R	O	A	S	T	I	N	G
P	L	S	H	A	D	O	W	N	D	F	A	R	A	D	S	R
B	L	O	W	N	A	W	C	G	E	Y	U	G	R	S	A	O
P	K	V	F	C	X	S	M	N	R	T	B	O	L	T	M	A
C	O	A	S	T	E	R	F	C	V	S	Q	A	W	O	Q	N
L	F	A	O	P	V	X	O	W	T	O	L	L	P	V	U	J
P	O	G	F	D	F	Y	A	O	I	L	W	Q	N	E	O	F
B	S	T	O	L	E	R	M	O	L	E	W	L	T	B	T	L
E	L	T	L	A	Q	N	B	F	U	J	L	L	O	W	E	R
M	O	L	D	I	S	T	O	N	E	Z	D	Y	A	S	M	W
X	R	H	K	L	S	B	O	F	E	P	F	L	O	W	N	P

CA **LC 1.7** Spell correctly roots, inflections, suffixes and prefixes, and syllable constructions.

Name ______________________________

Practice

Spelling: Long *o*

A. There are six spelling mistakes in this story about making a raft. Circle the misspelled words. Write the words correctly on the lines below.

Alex said, "I wonder if the eagle's nest was bloan away in the storm." The boys made a gole then. They chos to build a raft to sail across the lake and check on the eagle. They tied long, thick branches together with vines. To lowr the raft into the lake, they had to push it along the sand. You could hear them grone as they pushed. On the other side, they saw that the eagle's nest needed repair. They gathered twigs and left them for the bird to rebuild its nest. They choze to return home before it got dark.

1. ______________ 3. ______________ 5. ______________

2. ______________ 4. ______________ 6. ______________

B. Writing Activity

Write a short report about a raft trip to be read on a TV news show. Use four of the spelling words in your report.

____

____

____

____

____

____

____

____

CA **LC 1.7** Spell correctly roots, inflections, suffixes and prefixes, and syllable constructions.

Name ______________________

- You can correct a **run-on sentence** by rewriting it as a compound or a complex sentence.

Correct these run-on sentences by rewriting them as compound or complex sentences. Be sure that the new sentence makes sense.

1. I thought the visit would be boring I had a fun time.

____

2. I woke up the birds started chirping.

____

3. She looked at the drawings wondered who drew them.

____

____

4. He's never been on a boat he's afraid he'll get seasick.

____

____

5. Grandma is an artist is carving a bear.

____

6. You can go on the raft you must wear a life jacket.

____

____

7. The fawn was trapped I set her free.

____

8. We have to be careful the water is deep.

____

Name ______________________________

- A run-on sentence joins together two or more sentences.
- You can correct a run-on sentence by separating two complete ideas into two sentences.
- You can correct a run-on sentence by rewriting it as a compound or complex sentence.

Rewrite the journal entry below, correcting any punctuation and grammar mistakes. Be sure to fix any run-on sentences.

April 10 2005

Mom, Dad, Dave, and I went rafting on Foamy river today we had so much fun! We were worried about the water being cold it is only April. We brought extra sweaters. Of course, we also brought our lifejackets? Dave and I wanted to steer the raft we were too little. The current was very strong. The raft went up and down we got splashed a few times. We passed the woods my brother saw a deer. At the end of the day we were tired we want to go again soon.

____

____

____

____

____

____

____

____

____

Name ______________________________

1. Read the following sentence:

The room was crowded.

2. Think about what a crowded room is like.

3. Write 2–4 more sentences about the room that really SHOW that the room is crowded.

____

____

____

____

Extra Practice: Do the same exercise again, using the following sentence:

The house is very large.

____

____

____

____

____

____

____

____

____

Name ______________________________

When added to the beginning of a word, a prefix changes the meaning of the word.
The prefixes ***un***-, ***non***-, and ***dis***- mean "not" or "the opposite of."

- ***dis*** + trust = distrust to not trust
- ***non*** + sense = nonsense something that doesn't make sense
- ***un*** + covered = uncovered the opposite of covered

The prefix ***mis***- means "badly" or "incorrectly."

- ***mis*** + spell = misspell to spell incorrectly

Each of these prefixes has a short vowel sound.

Underline the prefix in the following words. Then write the meaning of the word.

1. disobey ______________________________

2. unsure ______________________________

3. misbehave ______________________________

4. nonsense ______________________________

5. unhappy ______________________________

6. dislike ______________________________

7. misunderstand ______________________________

8. disconnect ______________________________

9. unbelievable ______________________________

10. miscalculate ______________________________

Name ____________________

injustice	ancestors	unfair
numerous	segregation	avoided

Use the clues below to complete the vocabulary word puzzle.

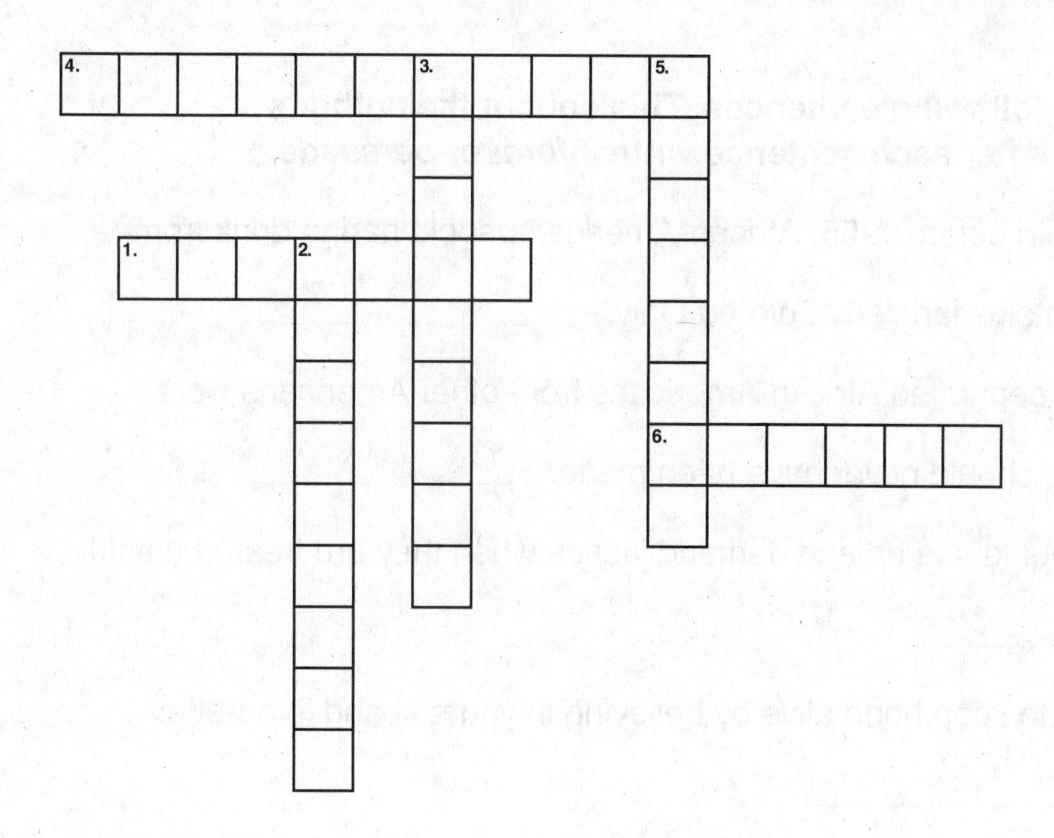

Across

1. kept away from
4. the practice of separating one racial group from another
6. unjust, unreasonable

Down

2. unfairness, an unjust act
3. people from whom one is descended
5. many

Name ______________________________

Authors write stories and plays to **entertain**. They write articles and books to **inform** or **explain**. When authors write to **persuade**, they give reasons for their point of view, which is what the authors believe and want you to believe, too. What they write is not always backed up by facts.

A. Read the following sentences. Think about the author's purpose. After each sentence write *inform* or *persuade.*

1. In the South before 1955, African-American people had to drink from water fountains labeled "Colored Only." ________________
2. Laws that separated African Americans from other Americans were unjust and should never have been made. ________________
3. People should rise up and demand justice when they are treated unfairly. ________________
4. You need to keep hope alive by believing in yourself and in a better world. ________________
5. In 1955, Rosa Parks was arrested for refusing to give up her seat near the front of a bus. ________________

B. Write a sentence to persuade readers to support your point of view on a topic you feel strongly about.

____

____

____

CA R 2.2 Use appropriate strategies when reading for different purposes (e.g., full comprehension, location of information, personal enjoyment).
R 2.0 Reading Comprehension

Name ___________________________________

As you read *My Brother Martin*, fill in the Author's Purpose Map.

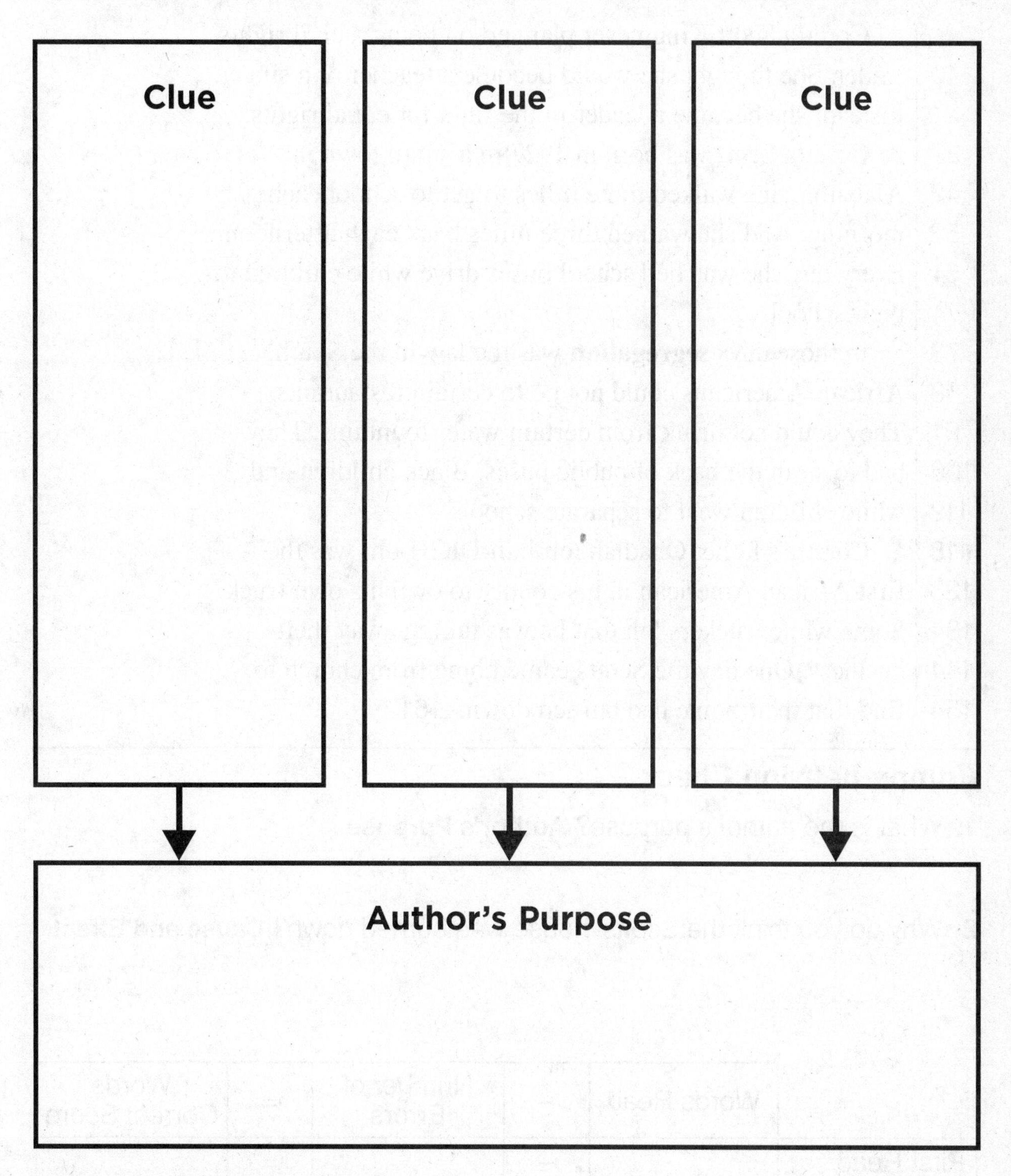

How does the information you wrote in the Author's Purpose Map help you to evaluate *My Brother Martin*?

Name ______________________________

As I read, I will pay attention to punctuation in each sentence.

	Coretta Scott King never planned on being a civil rights
10	leader. She thought she would become a teacher or a singer.
21	Instead, she became a leader in the fight for equal rights.
32	Coretta Scott was born in 1927 in a small town in
42	Alabama. She walked three miles to get to school each
52	morning. And she walked three miles back each afternoon.
61	Every day she watched school buses drive white children to
71	their school.
73	In those days **segregation** was the law in the South.
83	African Americans could not go to certain restaurants.
91	They could not drink from certain water fountains. They
100	had to sit in the back of public buses. Black children and
112	white children went to separate schools.
118	Coretta's father Obadiah (oh-buh-DIGH-uh) was the
123	first African American in his county to own his own truck.
134	Some white truckers felt that he was taking away their
144	business. One day the Scotts came home from church to
154	find that their home had burned down. 161

Comprehension Check

1. What is the author's purpose? **Author's Purpose**

2. Why do you think the Scotts' house was burned down? **Cause and Effect**

	Words Read	–	Number of Errors	=	Words Correct Score
First Read		–		=	
Second Read		–		=	

R 1.1 Read narrative and expository text aloud with grade-appropriate fluency and accuracy and with appropriate pacing, intonation, and expression.

Name ____________________

Letters have specific formats, but they all have the same three parts.

- A **salutation** is the line in the letter in which the writer greets the person to whom it was written.
- The **body** of the letter is the main part of the letter, containing the writer's message.
- The **complimentary closing** is the line above where the writer signs his or her name.

Read the letters below. Identify each part by drawing a line to the correct label below. On the blank, write whether it is a business or a personal letter.

7325 Hastings Road
San Diego, CA 90124
October 17, 2008

Hi, Jamal and Linda,

It was awesome to see you guys last week! The food was great and the company couldn't be beat.

Thanks again for having me over for the weekend. Next time, it's my turn.

Love,
Erica

____

7325 Hastings Road
San Diego, CA 90124

October 20, 2008

Levinson Randall, Inc.
62941 Chuckwalla Way
El Paso, TX 79901

Attn: Ms. Ann Gregory, Customer Service

Dear Ms. Gregory:

I am sending this letter to inform you that two of the four vases I ordered arrived damaged due to poor packaging.

Kindly send me two more of the Ballymoney crystal vases as soon as possible, and let me know how I should return the broken vases to you.

Sincerely,

Erica Eliades

____

Body

Salutation

Complimentary Closing

Name ______________________________

The prefix ***un-*** means “not.” ***Unfair*** means “not fair.”
The prefix ***re-*** means “again.” ***Retell*** means “tell again.”

Circle the phrases in the story that would sound better using the prefixes *un-* or *re-*. Then write the new words below.

“It’s terribly not fair, Grandmother!” Cordelia exclaimed. “Wilson School is just three blocks away. Why can’t I just keep attending my classes there?”

Cordelia’s grandmother looked at the bowl of cold, not eaten soup and left Cordelia’s question not answered. “Let me warm again that pea soup for you, honey. You’ll feel better after you have had your dinner.”

“I know you do not like this, Grandmother. Even though you’re not saying anything, I know you’re terribly not happy with the new laws. So, why can’t you admit that scheduling again our classes miles away is not acceptable!”

Marion looked over her glasses at her granddaughter. “No use talking about it around our kitchen table, child. But there will be talk all over this great land of ours. And mark my words, Cordelia, these not fortunate days will not go not noticed.”

CA R 1.0 Word Analysis, Fluency, and Systematic Vocabulary Development

Name ______________________________

Using the Word Study Steps

1. LOOK at the word.
2. SAY the word aloud.
3. STUDY the letters in the word.
4. WRITE the word.
5. CHECK the word.
   Did you spell the word right?
   If not, go back to step 1.

Add the Missing Prefix

Choose a prefix from the box below to add to each base word. Then write the spelling word you made. You may use a prefix more than once.

un- re- im- in- il- over- sub- pre- super-

1. ___ ___ ___ ___ ___ s i z e ______________
2. ___ ___ b l o c k ______________
3. ___ ___ l e a r n ______________
4. ___ ___ ___ ___ h e a t ______________
5. ___ ___ c o r r e c t ______________
6. ___ ___ p e r f e c t ______________
7. ___ ___ ___ w a y ______________
8. ___ ___ l e g a l ______________
9. ___ ___ ___ m i x ______________
10. ___ ___ c h a i n ______________
11. ___ ___ w i n d ______________
12. ___ ___ ___ ___ a c t ______________

CA LC 1.7 Spell correctly roots, inflections, suffixes and prefixes, and syllable constructions.

Name ______________________

A. Proofreading

There are six spelling mistakes in the story below. Circle the misspelled words. Write the words correctly on the lines below.

"It's so hot I think I'm going to overheet!" Elena said to Keisha. "Let's take the subbway instead of walking." "It will be my first time," Keisha said. "You'll have to show me what to do."

"It's easy," Elena said. "First we buy tickets. Then we need to make sure we get on the right train so we don't go to the uncorrect place. When the train arrives, the doors will inlock. We have to wait for the people who were riding to unlode. Then we can get on."

When the girls were on the train, Keisha gave her seat to a man with a hurt leg. She had sprained her ankle a few months ago and could recal how painful it was to stand. Elena smiled at her friend. "It looks like you already know the most important part—treating others with kindness and respect," she said.

1. ____________ 3. ____________ 5. ____________

2. ____________ 4. ____________ 6. ____________

B. Writing Activity

Write a story about a time when you treated someone else with kindness. Use at least three spelling words in your paragraph.

____

____

____

____

CA LC 1.7 Spell correctly roots, inflections, suffixes and prefixes, and syllable constructions.

Name ______________________________

- A **proper noun** names a particular person, place, or thing
  Examples: Ms. Brown San Francisco Atlantic Ocean
- A **proper noun** begins with a capital letter.
- Some proper nouns contain more than one word. Each important word begins with a capital letter.
  Examples: Statue of Liberty Boston Red Sox
- The name of a day, month, or holiday begins with a capital letter.

Read the list of nouns below. Decide whether each noun is common or proper and write it in the correct column. Capitalize the nouns in the Proper column.

independence day	summer	uniform	new york
hank aaron	stadium	ebbets field	july
home plate	jackie robinson	coach	world series
diamond	game	shortstop	ohio

COMMON	PROPER
______________________	______________________
______________________	______________________
______________________	______________________
______________________	______________________
______________________	______________________
______________________	______________________
______________________	______________________
______________________	______________________

Name ____________________

- Some proper nouns contain more than one word. Each important word begins with a capital letter.
- The name of a day, month, or holiday begins with a capital letter.

Rewrite the invitation below. Fix any spelling, punctuation, and grammar mistakes. Remember to capitalize each important word in a proper noun. Use a separate page if you need more space.

westfield little league invites you to attend

our 2005 most valuable player awards ceremony

at five o'clock on sunday, january 30

westfield town hall

501 central avenue, westfield, virginia

Please contact sally and jim smith at 555-1212 if you plan to attend.

We hope you will join us!

____

____

____

____

____

____

____

____

LC 1.0 Written and Oral English Language Conventions

Name ________________________________

Please read the following sentence:

Mary Beth shivered and zipped up her coat.

Think about what this sentence shows us about Mary Beth.

Underline the word that shows how Mary Beth felt.

Now read the following sentence:

Martin was scared to open the closet.

Write 2 more sentences that show how Martin felt.

Example:

Martin held his breath and peeked into the dark closet, trying not to think about the monster who lived there.

Martin got up his courage and opened the closet door, hoping all the clutter would not fall out.

____

____

____

____

____

____

____

____

Extra Practice: Read this sentence and add two more that show how Oscar felt.

Oscar was excited about going to the football game.

Name ______________________________

The letter pairs ***ch***, ***sh***, ***th***, ***wh***, and ***ph*** have one sound, even though there are two letters in the pair. Say the following words aloud and listen to the one sound made by the letter pairs.

- ***th*** thirty, bother
- ***ph*** phrase, headphone
- ***ch*** chair, archway
- ***sh*** shove, washer
- ***wh*** whirl, anywhere

Use the clues to fill in the blanks with words that have the *ch*, *sh*, *ph*, *wh*, or *th* sound.

1. I gave the money to my mother and ______________.
2. I made a ______________ before I blew out the candles on my birthday cake.
3. ______________ is the library? Is it near Flower Street?
4. My camera helps me take good ______________.
5. We stopped to rest on the park ______________.
6. I'm going to the dentist because I have a cavity in one ______________.
7. I picked up the ______________ and called my friend.
8. Today I have crackers and ______________ for a snack.
9. I put the plates, forks, and knives into the ______________ and turned it on.
10. I made a bar ______________ to show the daily sales of my lemonade stand.

Name ______________________________

Please read the following sentences:

Latoya hurt her finger.

Pete drank the entire glass of water in one gulp.

Underline the one that tells, instead of showing.

Think about how showing means that you use language that helps the reader picture exactly what is happening. Now rewrite that sentence so that it shows the reader what is happening rather then telling.

Example: Rushing to put away her laundry, Latoya jammed her finger in her top drawer.

Now, write 2 more showing sentences about that same moment.

Example: She jumped up and down and shook her hand, trying to stop her finger from throbbing. Tears welled up in her eyes and she wished she hadn't been in such a hurry in the first place.

____

____

____

____

____

____

____

Extra Practice: Do the same exercise with this sentence:

Steve felt sick.

Name ______________________________

In some **three-letter blends**, you hear the sounds of the three consonants, as in ***scrape*** and ***strain***. Sometimes, a three-letter blend is formed by a digraph and a third consonant, as in ***shrug*** and ***thread***.

A. Circle the three-letter blend at the beginning of each word.

1. splendid
2. shrink
3. throne
4. stream
5. splash
6. thread
7. shrimp
8. scrunch
9. split
10. through

B. Read the paragraph below. Circle six words that begin with a three-letter blend. Then continue the story. Use at least two words that begin with a three-letter blend and circle the words.

It was the first swim meet of the spring season. Juan climbed onto the starting block at the edge of the pool. He shrugged his shoulders to loosen his muscles, then plunged into the water, hardly making a splash. As his strong arms cut through the water, he saw his closest opponent about three feet behind him.

____

____

____

____

____

Name ______________________________

similar	challenges	designed
achieved	varied	

A. Write a complete sentence to answer each question below. In your answer, use the vocabulary word in bold type.

1. Why do you think goalball might be **similar** to soccer?

____

____

2. What is one of the **challenges** that an athlete with physical disabilities might face? ______________________________

____

3. What kind of athletic equipment might be specially **designed** for an athlete in the Paralympics? ______________________________

____

4. What are two of the **varied** games included in the Paralympics?

____

____

5. What is something that you **achieved** in the past last year?

____

B. Now use one of the words above in a sentence of your own.

6. ______________________________

____

Name ____________________

The **main idea** is what a paragraph is mostly about. A main idea can be **explicit**, or stated at the beginning of the paragraph. A main idea can also be **implied**, meaning that readers must think about how the details in the text are related.

Read the passage. Then answer the questions below.

Beep Baseball is a lot like baseball. It uses a ball. It uses bases. It has two teams. The players use a bat to hit the ball.

Unlike players on baseball teams, the players on Beep Baseball teams are sighted and non-sighted people. The sport is played with a big ball and a big bat. There are only two bases, which look like soft towers.

When a batter hits a ball, one of the bases begins to beep loudly. The batter runs toward the sound. If the batter can reach the base before someone throws a ball to the base, his or her team scores a point.

1. What is the main idea of the first paragraph?

The main idea of the first paragraph is Beep Baseball

2. Is that main idea explicit or implied?

The main idea was explicit. For example, Beep Base ball is alot like baseball.

3. What is a detail that supports that main idea?

"Beep Baseball is alot like baseball." Is means =. Beep Baseball = baseball

4. The main idea of the second paragraph is implied, or not stated. What is the main idea of this paragraph?

The main idea of the second paragraph is non-sighted and sighted people playing beep baseball.

5. Is the main idea of the third paragraph explicit or implied?

The main idea of the third paragraph is implied.

6. What would be a good main idea sentence for the third paragraph?

A good main idea sentence for the third paragraph is "What happens when the player hits the ball in Beep Baseball."

CA R 2.1 Identify structural patterns found in informational text (e.g., compare and contrast, cause and effect, sequential or chronological order, proposition and support) to strengthen comprehension.

Name ______________________________

As you read "Leg Work," fill in the Main Idea and Details Chart.

Main Idea

____

____

Detail 1 ______________________________

____

Detail 2 ______________________________

____

Summary

____

____

____

____

How does the information you wrote in the Main Idea and Details Chart help you understand the information presented in "Leg Work"?

R 2.1 Identify structural patterns found in informational text (e.g., compare and contrast, cause and effect, sequential or chronological order, proposition and support) to strengthen comprehension.

Name ______________________

As I read, I will focus on reading accurately.

| | “Are we there yet?” Jamal asked, crossing his arms
9 | across his chest.
12 | “Almost, honey,” his mom replied. “Look out the
20 | window. Isn’t it beautiful?”
24 | Jamal didn’t answer, but he did look. Out his mom’s
34 | window, all he could see was a rising, rocky cliff. Out his
46 | own window, the cliff dropped down, and Jamal could see
56 | the road winding below them. Below that were green
65 | fields. A few houses and farms were scattered about.
74 | The city was a long way away. It felt like they had been
87 | driving forever.
89 | They were driving up into the mountains to spend a
99 | week at a ranch. His mom had lived at this ranch when
111 | she was a little girl. “Some vacation,” Jamal thought to
121 | himself. 122

Comprehension Check

1. How does Jamal feel about his vacation? **Plot Development**

2. How does Jamal’s mom feel about the vacation? **Plot Development**

	Words Read	–	Number of Errors	=	Words Correct Score
First Read		–		=	
Second Read		–		=	

CA **R 1.1** Read narrative and expository text aloud with grade-appropriate fluency and accuracy and with appropriate pacing, intonation, and expression.

Name ______________________

Looking at the different parts of a book can help you figure out if the book will have the information you need.

title page	**table of contents**	**index**
glossary	**headings**	**subheadings**

Answer each question below by writing the name of the book part in the space provided.

1. What part of a book tells you the name of the author?

____

2. Where could you find the meaning of an unfamiliar word that was used in the book? ______________________

3. Where would you look to see if a particular topic is in the book?

____

4. What two book parts tell you what individual sections of a book are about?

____

5. What part of the book tells you the names of chapters in the book?

____

6. What two parts of a book are listed in alphabetical order?

____

CA **W 1.6** Locate information in reference texts by using organizational features (e.g., prefaces, appendixes).

Name ______________________________

Description Writing Frame

Summarize "Making a Splash." Use the Description Writing Frame below.

Rudy Garcia-Tolson has become a world-champion athlete.

To be a great swimmer, he ______________________________

____

____

____

______________________________.

He also ______________________________

____

____

____

______________________________.

In addition, his legs and feet ______________________________

____

____

____

______________________________.

All of these things have helped make him an Olympic champion!

Rewrite the completed summary on another sheet of paper. Keep it as a model for writing a summary of an article or selection using this text structure.

Name ______________________________

To understand the meaning of an **idiom**, you need to use the words and phrases around the idiom or think about how you might have heard the expression before.

A. Read the idioms in the box. Find and underline the idioms in the sentences below. Then circle the words in the sentence that help you understand the expression.

has a green thumb	get the hang of it
make a splash	lend a hand

1. I'd be happy to lend a hand and help you paint your room.
2. When you see all her healthy plants, it's easy to figure out that Mrs. Potts has a green thumb.
3. It took me a long time to learn how to download pictures onto my computer, but now that I get the hang of it, I do it all the time.
4. Unlike my friend who always likes to make a vivid impression on people, I don't usually like to make a splash.

B. Read the idioms below. Think about how you have heard them used. Then write a sentence that includes context clues that would help a reader understand each idiom.

5. catching a cold ______________________________

____

6. pull my leg ______________________________

____

Name ___________________________

Using the Word Study Steps

1. LOOK at the word.
2. SAY the word aloud.
3. STUDY the letters in the word.
4. WRITE the word.
5. CHECK the word.
   Did you spell the word right?
   If not, go back to step 1.

Find and Circle

Find and circle the hidden spelling words.

A	T	F	E	G	S	C	R	E	E	C	H
S	H	R	E	D	C	S	H	R	I	E	K
P	R	Q	S	P	R	O	U	T	W	P	O
L	O	Z	C	V	E	S	H	R	I	M	P
A	B	S	S	L	W	T	H	R	I	L	L
S	O	T	H	R	O	U	G	H	M	S	U
H	S	R	R	C	Y	K	M	B	S	T	T
I	C	A	I	T	H	R	O	A	T	R	J
N	R	P	N	S	P	L	I	T	R	A	K
G	I	S	K	A	A	S	P	R	A	N	G
M	P	N	S	P	R	A	W	L	I	D	M
S	T	R	A	I	G	H	T	E	N	K	I

CA LC 1.7 Spell correctly roots, inflections, suffixes and prefixes, and syllable constructions.

Name ______________________________

A. There are five spelling mistakes in this short story about Lei. Circle the misspelled words. Write the words correctly on the lines below.

Lei jumped rope with the girls at school. She played with her friends after school. She studied hard like her parents told her to. Lei was like other girls in most every way. But Lei had something no one else had—her grandmother's pink pearl necklace. Lei liked to wear the necklace around her throte on special days.

Lei received the pearl necklace when she was 11. The pearl was very old and special. It was a pearl that was worn by a princess in the ancient Chinese dynasties. It gave Lei such a threel to wear it.

One day, Lei was jumping rope at a party. All of a sudden, the shrand of pearls broke. The pearls flew off Lei's neck and scattered on the ground. Lei let out a shreak as she spraing to the ground to pick up the pearls. Her father saw what happened and helped Lei pick up the pearls. From then on, Lei was more careful with her necklace.

1. ______________ **3.** ______________ **5.** ______________

2. ______________ **4.** ______________

B. Writing Activity

Imagine that you are a prince or princess of an ancient Chinese dynasty. You have just received a pearl necklace like Lei's. Write a short story about what you would do with such a special necklace. Use at least four spelling words in your story.

____

____

____

____

____

CA **LC 1.7** Spell correctly roots, inflections, suffixes and prefixes, and syllable constructions.

Name ______________________________

- A few nouns have the same plural and singular form.
- To determine whether the noun is singular or plural, look at the rest of the sentence.

Read the sentences below. Then decide whether the underlined noun is *singular* or *plural*. Write your answer on the line.

1. There was not one sheep on Papa's farm. ____________
2. A herd of buffalo trampled across the land. ____________
3. Moose live in cold places, like Canada. ____________
4. This species of insect only lives for two days. ____________
5. I ate clams and shrimp at dinner. ____________
6. Be quiet or you might scare that deer away. ____________
7. We caught five fish today. ____________
8. We saw a moose at the zoo. ____________
9. He dipped each shrimp into the cocktail sauce. ____________
10. Sheep produce wool for sweaters. ____________
11. We raked the leaves today. ____________
12. I am not afraid of the mouse. ____________
13. She is getting her teeth cleaned. ____________
14. Several oxen passed the ranch. ____________
15. He wanted a baked potato. ____________

Name ____

- A few nouns have the same plural and singular form.
- To determine whether the noun is singular or plural, look at the rest of the sentence.

Rewrite the narrative below. Fix any spelling, punctuation, and grammar mistakes. Be sure to correct the 11 incorrectly formed plural nouns.

I want to be a chef who invents new, delicious dishs for people to enjoy! I decided this after visiting a new restaurant a few days ago. All of the mens, womans, and childs there watched the chef with great excitement. I watched him handle his long, sharp knifes carefully. Effortlessly, he diced potatos and tomatoeies into halfs and quarters. The shrimpses and fishies sizzled as he cooked them on the hot grill. When our excellent meal arrived, we really sank our toothes into it. That's when I decided cooking must be a fun way to be creative.

____

____

____

____

____

____

____

____

____

____

Name ______________________

Writing Rubric

4 Excellent	3 Good	2 Fair	1 Unsatisfactory
Ideas and Content/ Genre	Ideas and Content/ Genre	Ideas and Content/ Genre	Ideas and Content/ Genre
Organization and Focus	Organization and Focus	Organization and Focus	Organization and Focus
Sentence Structure/ Fluency	Sentence Structure/ Fluency	Sentence Structure/ Fluency	Sentence Structure/ Fluency
Conventions	Conventions	Conventions	Conventions
Word Choice	Word Choice	Word Choice	Word Choice
Voice	Voice	Voice	Voice
Presentation	Presentation	Presentation	Presentation

Name ______________________________

The suffixes **-y, -ly, -ful, -less,** and **-ness** can be added to the end of a root or base word to change its meaning. Sometimes spelling changes are necessary:

penny – y + i + less = penniless
sun + n + y = sunny

Add the suffix to the end of each word. Remember to make any necessary spelling changes. Write the new word. Then use the word in a sentence.

1. happy + ly = ____________

____

2. thought + ful = ____________

____

____

3. care + less = ____________

____

4. kind + ness = ____________

____

____

5. fun + y = ____________

____

6. cheer + ful + ly = ____________

____

7. grace + ful + ness = ____________

____

8. hope + less + ly = ____________

____

mysterious	responsibility	midst
loosened	amazement	sores

A. Choose the correct vocabulary word from the list to complete the sentence. Write the words on the lines.

David had a dog. He knew it was his **1.** ____________________ to take care of Spot. Of course, they had fun together. They played and ran and explored. Then one day, in the **2.** ____________________ of having fun, Spot ran through some poison ivy. He soon was covered with painful **3.** ____________________. David took his dog home and washed Spot as best he could. He wrapped Spot up in a quilt and sat with him on the porch. At first, Spot tried to scratch. Then a **4.** ____________________ thing began to happen. Spot stopped wriggling and trying to scratch. David **5.** ____________________ the quilt and looked at Spot's legs in **6.** ____________________. They were still red and swollen. Somehow, having his owner take care of him had calmed him down.

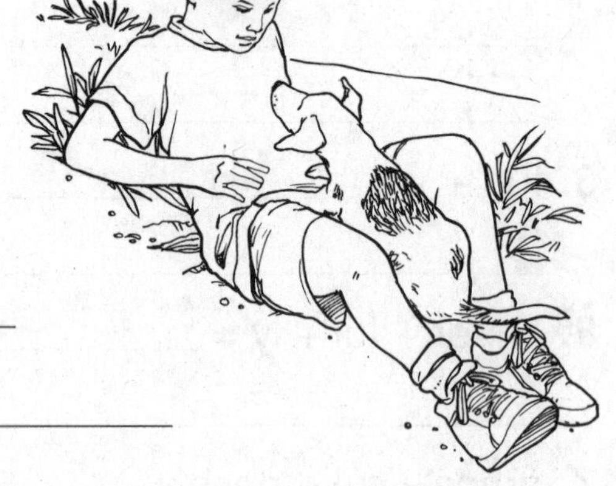

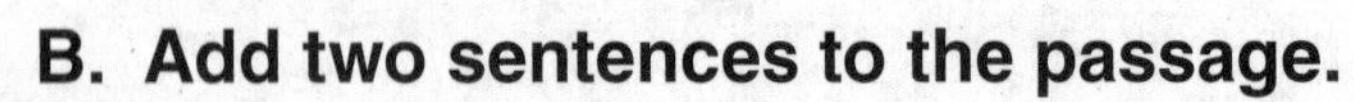

B. Add two sentences to the passage.

7. ____

____

____

8. ____

Name ______________________________

Recognizing the **sequence**, or order, in which things happen in a story, helps you better understand what you read.

A. Read the passage below. Then number the sentences below to show the sequence of events.

The Plains Indians lived in North America before the Europeans came. Since they had no horses, the Plains Indians traveled on foot. To hunt buffalo, they would surround a herd and shoot the buffalo with bows and arrows.

This changed when Spanish explorers came to North America and brought horses with them. Now the Plains Indians hunters were able to ride horses and follow buffalo over long distances. They carried tipis with them and set up camps. The hunters could kill buffalo and pull them back to camp using their horses.

Later, guns again changed the way that Plains Indians hunted.

1. _____ Spanish explorers brought horses to North America.

2. _____ The Plains Indians used horses and traveled long distances to hunt buffalo.

3. _____ The Plains Indians hunted buffalo on foot before the Europeans came to North America.

4. _____ The Plains Indians used guns to hunt buffalo.

B. Add an event to the paragraphs and tell where it belongs in the sequence of events.

____

____

CA **R 2.1** Identify structural patterns found in informational text (e.g., compare and contrast, cause and effect, **sequential** or chronological order, proposition and support) to strengthen comprehension.

Name ______________________________

As you read *Mystic Horse*, fill in the Sequence Chart.

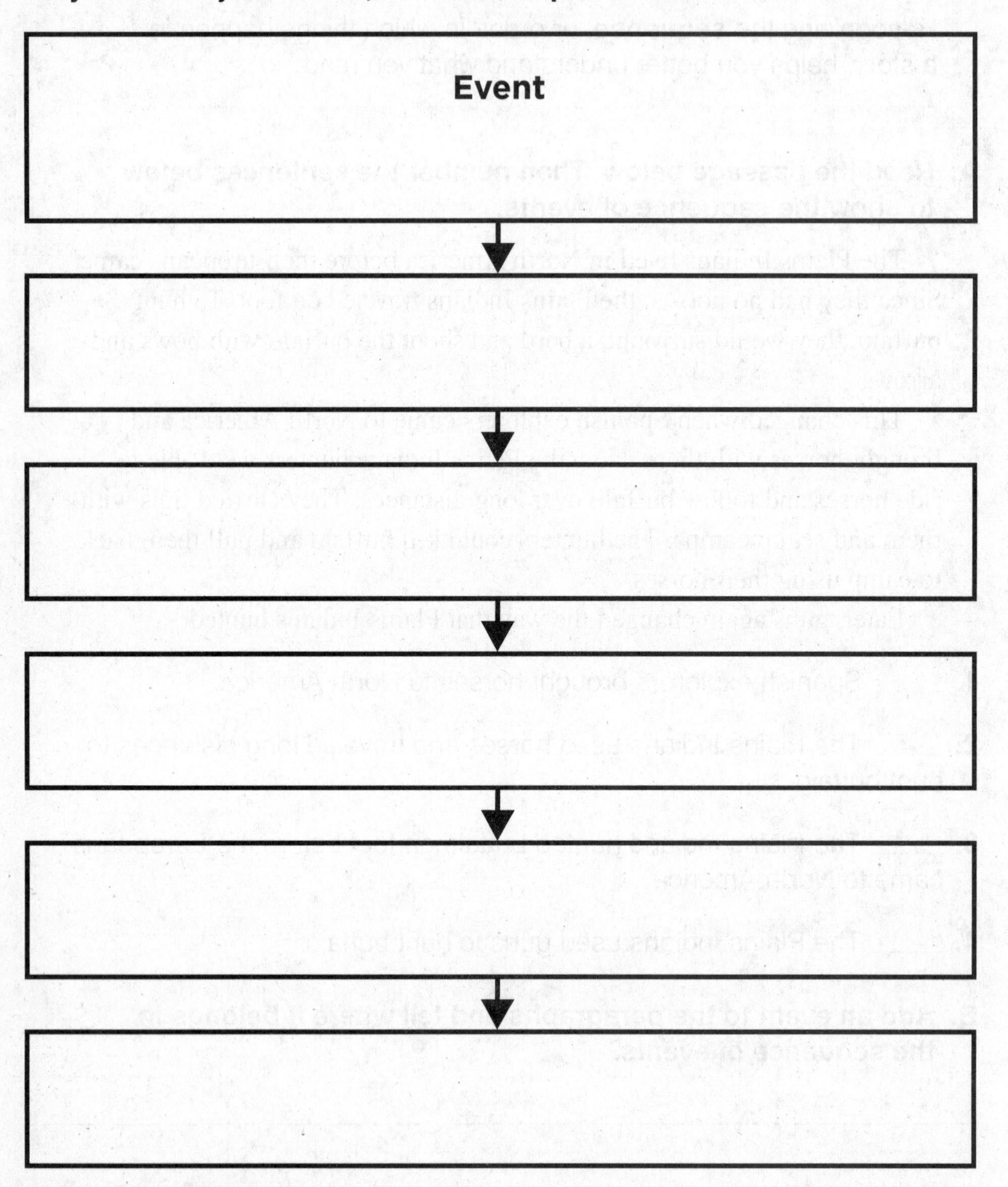

How does the information you wrote in the Sequence Chart help you to summarize *Mystic Horse*?

R 2.1 Identify structural patterns found in informational text (e.g., compare and contrast, cause and effect, **sequential** or chronological order, proposition and support) to strengthen comprehension.

Name ______________________________

As I read, I will pay attention to the pacing and intonation of the passage.

But there came a time when many days of heavy rain
11 made the Quillayute River overflow. The houses washed
19 away. Then the Quileute moved to the prairies.
27 Not long after, the weather grew cold. The rain turned
37 into hail and sleet. The fishermen could not break through
47 the ice in the rivers to go fishing. Falling hailstones were
58 so big that people were killed. The people grew afraid to
69 go outside. They were running out of food. Men, women,
79 and children were becoming weak and sick.
86 At this time, the Great Chief of the Quileute called a
97 meeting of all the people in the tribe. He stood before them
109 in a patchwork shawl made up of buffalo skins stitched
119 together. The people begged the chief to do something. The
129 **responsibility** of watching over his people weighed heavily
137 upon him. "We will ask the Great Spirit who soars above
148 Earth for help," said the chief. 154

Comprehension Check

1. What were the events that caused the Great Chief of the Quileute to call a meeting? Name the events in the order in which they occurred. **Sequence**

2. What is the purpose of a legend such as this? **Author's Purpose**

	Words Read	–	Number of Errors	=	Words Correct Score
First Read		–		=	
Second Read		–		=	

CA **R 1.1** Read narrative and expository text aloud with grade-appropriate fluency and accuracy and with appropriate **pacing**, **intonation**, and expression.

Name ______________________________

A **table** presents factual information—such as names, places, and numbers—in a compact form.

Look at the table from a sports almanac. Then use the table to answer the questions that follow.

The Top Five Pitchers in Baseball History

Name	Career Length	Games Won	Games Lost
Walter Johnson	21 years	417	279
Christy Matthewson	17 years	373	188
Sandy Koufax	12 years	165	87
Lefty Grove	17 years	300	141
Cy Young	22 years	511	316

1. What does this table tell you about these pitchers? ______________

____

2. Which of the pitchers had the shortest career? ______________

3. Which pitcher won the most games? ______________

4. Which pitcher lost the fewest number of games? ______________

5. Which pitchers had careers that lasted the same number of years?

____

6. Who has the highest numbers in all three categories? ______________

Name ______________________________

Homophones are pairs of words that are pronounced the same but have different spellings and meanings.

here / hear	needed / kneaded	plains / planes
there / their	seen / scene	buries / berries
rain / rein	four / for	road / rode
blue / blew	through / threw	

Read the passage. Write *correct* on the lines below if the right homophone is used. If the wrong homophone is used, write the correct word on the line.

Some Native Americans lived on the planes [1] in the middle of our country. The land their [2] is beautiful. The sky is blue [3] and tall grass seems to go on forever. Even today, the miles of grass are a beautiful scene [4]. The Native Americans road [5] their horses threw [6] the plains [7] hunting four [8] buffalo to eat. They also ate berries [9] and nuts to add to there [10] diet. It was a hard life but the Native Americans were proud of the life they lived.

1. ____________________ **6.** ____________________

2. ____________________ **7.** ____________________

3. ____________________ **8.** ____________________

4. ____________________ **9.** ____________________

5. ____________________ **10.** ____________________

Name ______________________________

Using the Word Study Steps

1. LOOK at the word.
2. SAY the word aloud.
3. STUDY the letters in the word.
4. WRITE the word.
5. CHECK the word.
   Did you spell the word right?
   If not, go back to step 1.

Add the Suffix

Add the suffix in parentheses to the base word. Then write the spelling word. Remember to make any necessary spelling changes to the base word.

1. beauty (-ful) ____________
2. thought (-ful) ____________
3. sick (-ly) ____________
4. wonder (-ful) ____________
5. quick (-ly) ____________
6. shape (-less) ____________
7. good (-ness) ____________
8. spoon (-ful) ____________
9. ill (-ness) ____________
10. age (-less) ____________
11. spot (-less) ____________
12. dark (-est) ____________

CA **LC 1.7** Spell correctly roots, inflections, suffixes and prefixes, and syllable constructions.

Name ______________________________

A. Proofreading

There are six spelling mistakes in the story below. Circle the misspelled words. Write the words correctly on the lines below.

Red's grandmother had an ilness. Red didn't like the darknes of the woods around Grandmother's house, but she wanted to help Grandmother feel better. She decided to be brave and bring Grandmother a basket of food.

Red quicklie ran through the woods to get to Grandmother's house. She was almost there when she saw a dark, shapless figure ahead. She hoped it wasn't Wolf.

"Who's there?" she called.

"It's just me," Grandmother replied. "My weakeness has gone away, so I came to meet you."

"Thank goodnes it's you!" said Red.

1. ______________ 3. ______________ 5. ______________

2. ______________ 4. ______________ 6. ______________

B. Writing Activity

Write a story about a time when you or someone you know did something brave. Use at least three spelling words in your paragraph.

____

____

____

____

CA **LC 1.7** Spell correctly roots, inflections, suffixes and prefixes, and syllable constructions.

Name 100%

- A **plural noun** names more than one person, place, or thing.
- Add **-s** to most nouns to form the plural. Do not use an apostrophe.
- A **possessive noun** shows who or what owns or has something.
- Add an apostrophe (') and **-s** to a singular noun to make it possessive.

Write a plural noun or a possessive noun to complete each sentence. Use the singular nouns in the box to help you.

box picture snake rattle skin prairie book

1. She carried the noisy rattles from several snakes.
2. When he saw the rattlesnake, he was scared by the Snake's sound.
3. I want to find some books about animals in the library.
4. This book has words but no pictures.
5. This Snake's photographs are very interesting.
6. Snakes shed their skin when they grow.
7. Will you help me open those boxes to see what's inside?
8. A Snake's bite may or may not contain poison.
9. Oh no, that boxe's lid is moving!
10. Some types of snakes live in fields and prairies.

Name ____________________

- A **plural noun** names more than one person, place, or thing.
- A **possessive noun** shows who or what owns or has something.

Correctly rewrite the letter below.

December 9, 2008

Ms Margaret Wilson
Atlanta Public library
101 Reading Road
Atlanta, GA 33560

Dear ms Wilson

I am writing to complain about the poor service in the childrens section of your library. Last saturday, I wanted to check out the North American Snake Guide by Doctor david Howard. I waited for more than 30 minute's before anyone came to help me. No ones should have to wait that long.

Yours truly,
Kevin Andrews, Junior

____

____

____

____

____

____

____

____

____

CA **LC 1.4** Use parentheses, commas in direct quotations, and **apostrophes** in the possessive case of nouns and in contractions.
LC 1.0 Written and Oral English Language Conventions

Name ______________________________

After each verb below, please write three showing verbs with a similar meaning.

Example: Run gallop, sprint, jog.

Cry

Eat

Hit

Fall

Need

Go

Look

Extra Practice: For each of the words below, give three showing verbs with a similar meaning.

Break

Clean

Say

CA W 1.0 Writing Strategies

Name ________________________________

Practice

Phonics:
r-Controlled Vowels
er, ir, ur

The **/ûr/** sound can be spelled ***er, ir,*** and ***ur.*** The sound is found in words such as ***serpent, bird,*** and ***turkey.***

A. Underline the *vowel + r combination* that represents the /ûr/ sound in each of these words.

1. burden
2. sternly
3. serpent
4. birth
5. turnip
6. whirlwind
7. burrow
8. purpose
9. person
10. girlfriend

B. Now read the paragraph below. Find and circle six words that have the /ûr/ sound. Then continue the story. Circle the words with the /ûr/ sound.

One day, a raccoon climbed in the window of a house. He found a skirt on the floor. Holding it carefully in his mouth, he took it outside. Then he returned and carried away a small purse. Finally, he emerged with a purple shirt.

____

____

____

____

____

____

Name ________________________________

apologize	genuine	harmless
slithered	ambulance	weekdays

A. Use the correct vocabulary word from the box to fill in the blank.

1. On our hike a snake ________________ across the trail.

2. The reptile exhibit at the zoo is open ________________ from 10 A.M. to 5 P.M.

3. My encyclopedia says that the green snake we saw in my garden is ________________.

4. An ________________ rushed the snakebite victim to the hospital.

5. Evan should ________________ for leaving a rubber snake on his sister's pillow.

6. Danielle's snake is ________________, not rubber!

B. Write a sentence using one of the vocabulary words.

7. ____
____

8. ____

Name ________________________

Sometimes you have to use story clues and what you know from your own experiences to help you **make inferences** about what's happening in the plot of a story.

Read the story. Then make inferences to answer the questions.

Evangeline didn't look up from her book when the new student said hello. The book was called *Adventures with Reptiles.* She'd already read it twice, but she just couldn't put it down. At the end of a chapter, she finally looked up from her book.

"I have that book," Jae said. "It's great. Do you want to come over after school to meet my pet lizard?"

"You bet!"

1. How does Evangeline feel when Jae says hello? How do you know?

____

____

2. Is the book Evangeline is reading one of her favorites? Why or why not?

____

____

3. What kinds of books would the new student like to read? How do you know? ________________________

____

4. Do you think Evangeline and the new student will become friends? Why or why not? ________________________

____

Name ___________________________

As you read *When I Went to the Library*, fill in the Inferences Web.

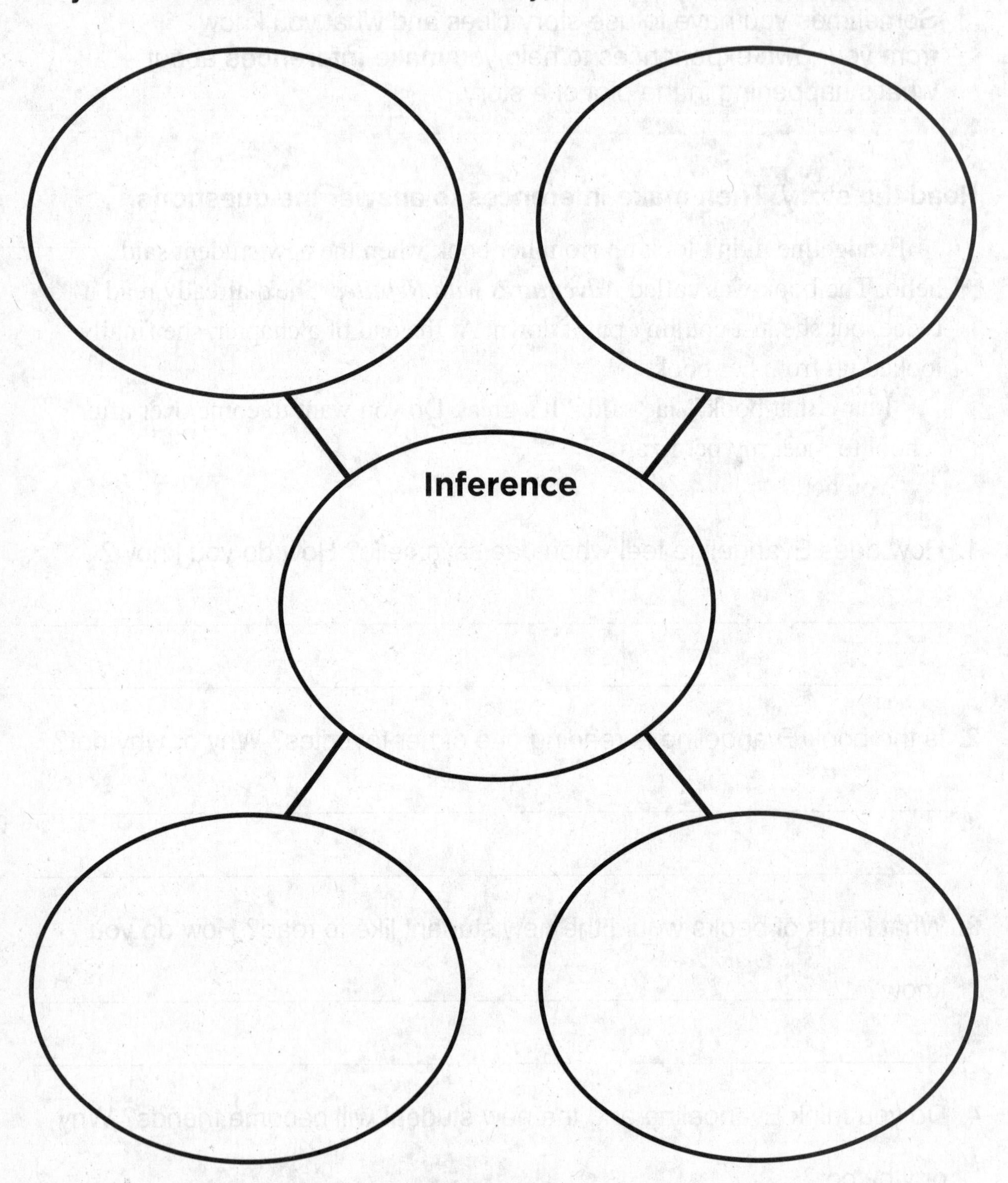

How does the information you wrote in the Inferences Web help you to generate questions about *When I Went to the Library*?

Name ______________________________

As I read, I will pay attention to pacing and intonation.

North America is a large area of land. It contains
10 many different climates and landscapes. Most of Mexico
18 and the southwestern United States is hot and dry. Other
28 areas, including the northeastern states and parts of Canada,
37 are cool and wet. Some areas have large mountain ranges,
47 like the Rocky Mountains in the West. Others have flat,
57 rolling plains, like the Midwest.
62 Snakes can be found in just about all of these places.
73 Snakes live in forests, canyons, and deserts. One might
82 even be living in your own backyard. Most snakes don't do
93 well in the cold. In fact, the hardy garter snake is the only
106 serpent that can survive in Alaska.
112 North America has five snake families. Two of these
121 families are poisonous, and three are not. Meet the five
131 families. As you read this book, you will get to know them
143 a lot better. 146

Comprehension Check

1. What is the main idea about snakes in this passage? **Main Idea and Details**

2. Why is there only one kind of snake in Alaska? **Cause and Effect**

	Words Read	–	Number of Errors	=	Words Correct Score
First Read		–		=	
Second Read		–		=	

CA **R 1.1** Read narrative and expository text aloud with grade-appropriate fluency and accuracy and with appropriate **pacing**, **intonation**, and expression.

Name ______________________________

An encyclopedia is a set of books with information on a wide variety of topics. An electronic encyclopedia has the same information but it is on a CD-ROM. You can use the **toolbar** to find the information you want.

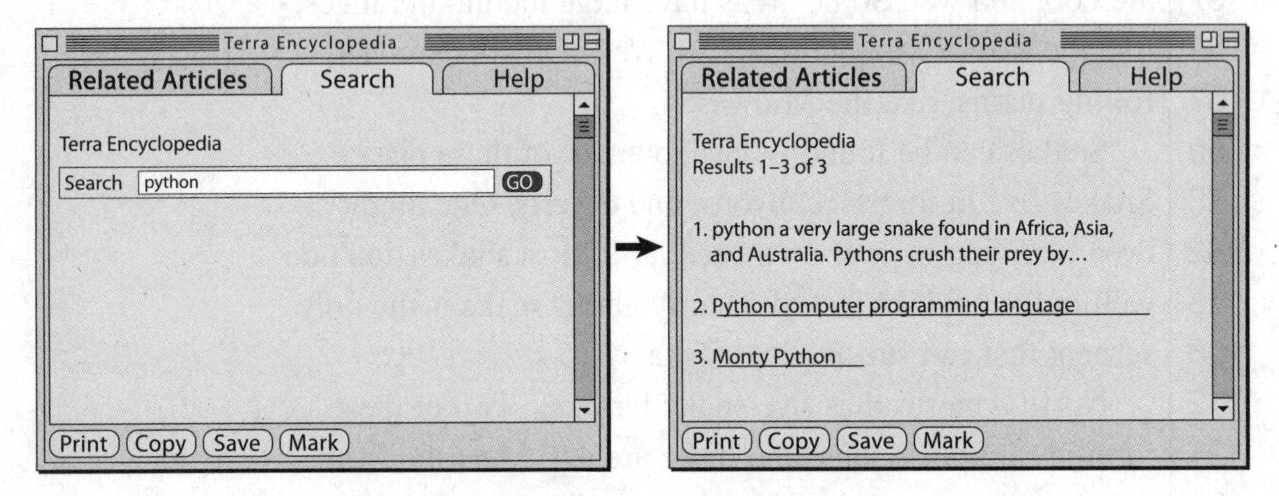

Study the pages above to answer these questions.

1. What information is the computer user looking for? ______________________________

____

2. How many entries are shown for *python* in the encyclopedia?

____

3. Which button on the toolbar should the user click on to print out a copy of the page? ______________________________

4. If you are looking for a good map of Australia, what button on the toolbar would you click? ______________________________

5. If you are looking for more information about snakes, what button would you click? ______________________________

Name ______________________________

Prefixes and **suffixes** can be added to many words. The original word is called the **base word**. If you know what the base word is, you can figure out the meaning of the word with a prefix or suffix. You can find the meaning of prefixes and suffixes in a dictionary.

unhappy
The base word is ***happy***. ***Happy*** means "feeling good."
The prefix ***un-*** means "the opposite of."
The word ***unhappy*** means "not feeling good."

Find the word with a prefix or suffix in each sentence. Circle the base word. Then tell what the word with the suffix or prefix means.

1. The snake's markings were colorful, with red and blue bands.

   ____

2. Even small snakes can be dangerous sometimes.

   ____

3. Knowing that the snake was hidden somewhere in the room made us all uncomfortable.

   ____

4. The water moccasin swam under Khalid's boat and disappeared.

   ____

5. Casey was successful in finding a picture of a rattlesnake in the book.

   ____

Name ______________________________

Using the Word Study Steps

1. LOOK at the word.
2. SAY the word aloud.
3. STUDY the letters in the word.
4. WRITE the word.
5. CHECK the word.
   Did you spell the word right?
   If not, go back to step 1.

Find Rhyming Words

Circle the word in each row that rhymes with the spelling word on the left.

1. twirl	whirl	twist
2. blurred	married	stirred
3. curve	cave	serve
4. birth	mirth	bath
5. hurl	earl	haul
6. shirt	sure	dirt
7. purse	please	curse
8. curl	girl	call
9. turkey	tacky	murky
10. sternly	firmly	silly
11. pearl	pail	whirl
12. curb	herb	cure

CA **LC 1.7** Spell correctly roots, inflections, suffixes and prefixes, and syllable constructions.

Name ______________________________

A. Proofreading

There are five spelling mistakes in the paragraphs below. Circle the misspelled words. Write the words correctly on the lines below.

The tree was tired of standing in one place all the time and never moving. The tree wanted to move. During the winter, the tree wanted to kirl up for warmth. In the summer, the tree wanted to swim and swurl through the water. Never in its whole life had the tree left its spot. It wanted to travel the earth.

One day a snake slithered by. The tree said, "I wish I could travel the world like you." "Really?" replied the sirpent. "Here I was thinking I'd rather be a tree. I wouldn't have to search for my food every day. And I could let my branches and leaves twirle around in the wind while I stood still."

At that, the tree started thinking. "That's true, I don't have to run around all the time, and that's pretty nice." From then on, the tree understood how lucky it was to be able to stand, and found a perpose in life.

1. ________________ **3.** ________________ **5.** ________________

2. ________________ **4.** ________________

B. Writing Activity

Imagine that you've met someone who has taught you a lesson. Who was the person and what did you learn from him or her? Use at least four spelling words in your paragraph.

____

____

____

____

____

____

CA **LC 1.7** Spell correctly roots, inflections, suffixes and prefixes, and syllable constructions.

Name ______________________________

- Add **-es** to verbs that end in ***s, ch, sh, x,*** or ***z*** if the subject is singular.
- Change ***y*** to ***i*** and add **-es** to verbs that end with a consonant and ***y***.
- Do not add **-s** or **-es** to a present-tense verb when the subject is plural or ***I*** or ***you***.

Read each sentence. Write the correct present-tense form of each underlined verb on the lines provided.

1. The rattlesnake stretch out along the rocks. ________________
2. His scales flashes silver in the hot desert sun. ________________
3. He swish his long tail. ________________
4. A prairie dog scurry away when it hears the snake's rattle.
   ____
5. A small lizard crawl away. ________________
6. The rattlesnake reach the edge of the rock. ________________
7. A bee buzz past the snake. ________________
8. The rattlesnake hurry down the rock. ________________
9. He quickly pass by a cold, shaded area. ________________
10. You approaches any snake with caution. ________________

Name ____________________

- The present tense must have subject-verb agreement.
- Add ***-s*** to most verbs if the subject is singular.
- Add ***-es*** to verbs that end in ***s, ch, sh, x,*** or ***z*** if the subject is singular.
- Change ***y*** to ***i*** and add ***-es*** to verbs that end in a consonant and ***-y***.

Proofread the dialogue below. Look for mistakes in present tense subject-verb agreement and quotations. Rewrite the dialogue, action verbs, and quotations correctly.

I am so excited! Today I leaves on a trip to Taos, New Mexico! Carla say.
Dad reply, we should be there in about an hour.
Mom point to the mountains in the distance. She say, stop the car so we can takes some pictures.
Carla remark, I see a strange bird in the distance.
Dad explain, the bird is a roadrunner.
Carla watch the speedy bird. It pass close enough to see its feathers.

____

____

____

____

____

____

____

____

____

1. Please read the following sentences:

alice was so angry she wanted to scream. her brother broke her stereo by accident. she burst into tears and just wanted to be left alone. her brother was extremely upset that he had broken his sister's stereo by accident.

2. Now, circle the words that should start with capital letters. Remember, EVERY sentence starts with a capital letter.

Extra Practice: Do the same exercise with the following sentences:

amy loved horseback riding. each weekend she would wait for her lesson with anticipation. it always seemed to take forever to get to the stable and once she was there, she would have so much fun, her lesson would fly by.

Name ______________________________

Say the words below aloud. In each word, the letter in dark type is silent.

knives plum**b**er ca**l**m **w**riggle

A. Quietly read the sentences aloud to yourself. Then circle the letter in the underlined word that you did not pronounce.

1. Rosa Parks knew that staying in her seat was the right thing to do.
2. Taking a risk might make the palms of your hands sweaty.
3. Christine kneeled down on the floor to pick up the paper she had dropped.
4. Martin's father needed a wrench to fix the piano bench.
5. The tombs in the cemetery remind us of those who came before us.

B. Using a dictionary, find at least five other words that begin with *kn* and *wr*. Write these words on the lines below and circle the silent letter in each one.

***kn-* words**	***wr-* words**
____________	____________
____________	____________
____________	____________
____________	____________
____________	____________

CA **R 1.0** Word Analysis, Fluency, and Systematic Vocabulary Development

Name ____________________

A. Use the words in the box to complete the sentences below.

neglected	desperate	obedience
appreciated	endured	misunderstood

1. I play with my dog a lot so she does not feel ____________.

2. The only time I scold Sparky is when he tries to eat food from our table. Each time he looks at me as if he has ____________ great suffering.

3. Once I sent him to ____________ school.

4. Jill ____________ the toys we gave to her dog, especially the ball.

B. Write two sentences, each using one of the vocabulary words.

5. ______________________________

____

6. ______________________________

____

Name ______________________________

A cause makes something happen. An effect is what happens. Story plots contain several causes and effects. Using what you know and what the author tells you to **draw conclusions** can help you figure out the plot.

Read the story. Draw conclusions to answer the questions.

Fred and Roberto lived next door to each other. Whenever Roberto looked out the window and saw that Fred's owner was taking him for a walk, Roberto would scratch at the front door and whine until Mrs. Marsh got his leash and took him out.

One day, Fred came bounding into Roberto's backyard. "I'm running away," he told Roberto. "Mr. Gomez doesn't appreciate the way I bring him his slippers when he comes home from work."

"Don't do it," Roberto advised Fred. "Give Mr. Gomez a little more time to get to know you. He will appreciate you when he gets to know you better."

"You may be right," Fred agreed. "I'll give him another chance."

1. Draw a conclusion. What caused Roberto to scratch on the door?

____

2. What effect did Roberto's scratching have?

____

3. What kind of personality does Roberto have?

____

4. Why does Fred agree with Roberto?

____

Name ______________________________

Practice

Comprehension: Conclusions Chart

As you read *Dear Mrs. LaRue*, fill in the Conclusions Chart.

Text Clues	Conclusions

How does completing the Conclusions Chart help you draw conclusions about *Dear Mrs. LaRue*?

R 2.0 Reading Comprehension

Name ______________________________

As I read, I will pay attention to expression.

	Presidents have kept a wide range of pets. These
9	animals have included cows, mice, goats, and birds. But
18	dogs have been the most popular presidential pets.
26	Dogs are loyal and loving. They make their owners
35	feel appreciated. Like other dog owners, many Presidents
43	have enjoyed the special friendship that dogs can give.
52	Many people believe that dogs help Presidents gain
60	support from Americans. Pictures of Presidents playing
67	with their dogs can make the Presidents seem likable and
77	help them win votes.
81	More than 200 dogs of various breeds have lived at the
91	White House. Some of these White House dogs served
100	as guard dogs. Others played with the Presidents' children.
109	And others clearly belonged to the Presidents and were
118	their personal four-legged friends. A few presidential
125	pooches were even as well known as their masters. Let's
135	take a look at some of the famous "First Dogs" of America. 147

Comprehension Check

1. Why might people vote for a candidate who has a dog as a pet? **Cause and Effect**

2. Why did the author write this passage about presidential dogs? **Author's Purpose**

	Words Read	–	Number of Errors	=	Words Correct Score
First Read		–		=	
Second Read		–		=	

CA **R 1.1** Read narrative and expository text aloud with grade-appropriate fluency and accuracy and with appropriate pacing, intonation, and **expression**.

Practice

Text Feature: Line Graphs

Name ______________________________

A **line graph** is a good way to show how something changes over time. Points on the graph are connected by lines that make it easy to tell whether the occurrences of something increased or decreased as time passed.

Look at the line graph below and answer the questions.

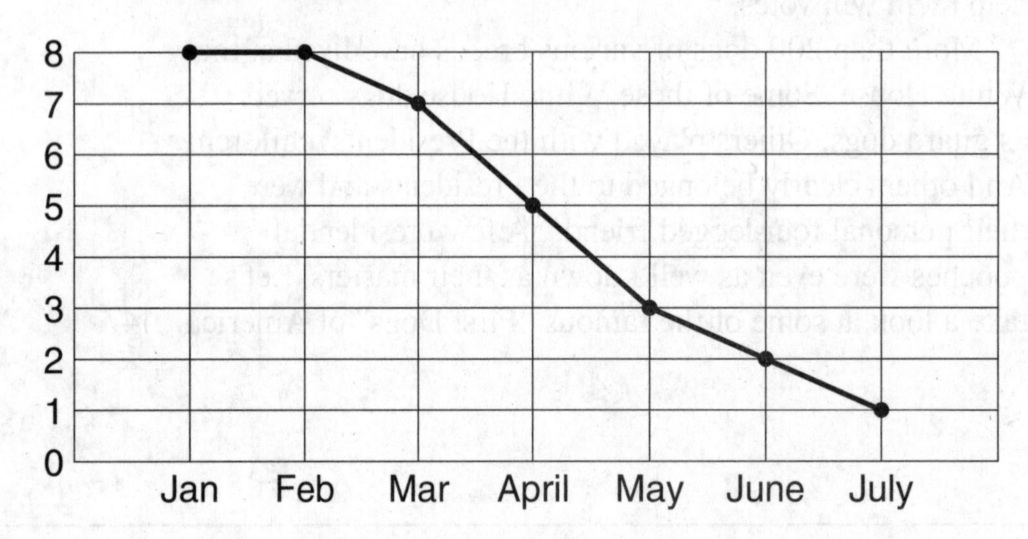

1. During which two months were the largest number of search dogs needed? ______________________

2. How many search dogs were needed in May? ____________

3. In which month were 5 search dogs needed? ____________

4. Which two months had the same number of searches?

____

5. How many more searches were requested in January than in July?

____

Name ______________________________

When you put the **prefix** *mis-* in front of a word, it changes the meaning of the word. *Mis-* means "badly" or "incorrectly."

Add the prefix *mis-* to each word. Then write a sentence with the new word.

New word

1. judge ____________
2. spell ____________
3. treat ____________
4. read ____________
5. behave ____________

Sentence

1. ______________________________
____
2. ______________________________
____
3. ______________________________
____
4. ______________________________
____
5. ______________________________
____

CA R 1.0 Word Analysis, Fluency, and Systematic Vocabulary Development

Name ________________________________

Using the Word Study Steps

1. LOOK at the word.
2. SAY the word aloud.
3. STUDY the letters in the word.
4. WRITE the word.
5. CHECK the word.
   Did you spell the word right?
   If not, go back to step 1.

Find and Circle

Find and circle the hidden spelling words.

P	L	U	M	B	E	R	K	Y	U	I	Q
Z	C	O	M	B	S	K	N	I	V	E	S
W	R	I	N	K	L	E	E	R	R	T	F
R	W	R	E	N	C	H	W	D	F	G	V
A	Q	R	H	O	U	R	H	O	N	O	R
P	A	N	S	W	E	R	L	A	M	B	S
P	B	H	O	N	E	S	T	Y	V	B	H
E	N	O	L	N	X	K	N	E	A	D	Z
R	K	N	E	E	L	F	B	S	D	E	Q
A	H	E	I	R	W	R	I	G	G	L	E
A	K	S	P	D	O	U	B	T	D	R	T
W	L	T	H	U	M	B	S	Q	R	C	A

CA **LC 1.7** Spell correctly roots, inflections, suffixes and prefixes, and syllable constructions.

Name ______________________________

A. Proofreading

There are six spelling mistakes in the story below. Circle the misspelled words. Write the words correctly on the lines below.

My brother Sam could never make up his mind about what he wanted to be when he grew up. He just new that he wanted to help people.

At one time, he wanted to be a farmer. He liked sheep and lams. I think he would have liked herding them. He could have been a shepherd.

Sam also liked tools. He liked fixing his bike with a rench. He could have been a plummer. He would have liked helping people by fixing their leaky sinks.

When he decided to be a judge, I was sure that was the perfect job for him. He was always onest and fair. I had no dout that he would help a lot of people. You could just tell that he was going to make a difference, whether as a shepherd, a plumber, or a judge.

1. ____________ 3. ____________ 5. ____________

2. ____________ 4. ____________ 6. ____________

B. Writing Activity

Think about people like Dr. Martin Luther King and others who make a difference. Write a paragraph describing another job that involves helping people. Use at least four spelling words in your paragraph.

CA **LC 1.7** Spell correctly roots, inflections, suffixes and prefixes, and syllable constructions.

Name ______________________

Practice

Grammar: Verb Tenses

- A verb in the **future tense** tells about an action that is going to happen.
- To write about the future, use the special verb ***will.***

Underline the action verb in each sentence. Rewrite the sentence so it tells about the future.

1. The teachers assign a project about the Civil Rights movement.

____

2. The students work in pairs.

____

3. All of the classes go to the library.

____

4. Cordell and Janine find out about the Voting Rights Act of 1965.

____

5. Yvonne and Frank learn about educational rights.

____

6. The librarians show us the right books and magazines.

____

7. Juan and Patricia give an oral report.

____

8. Josie and Emmett create a poster.

____

CA **LC 1.3** Identify and use regular and irregular **verbs**, adverbs, prepositions, and coordinating conjunctions in writing and speaking.

Name ______________________________

- A verb in the **past tense** tells about an action that already happened.
- A verb in the **future tense** tells about an action that is going to happen.

Rewrite the poem below. Change the underlined verbs to the past tense. Then circle the verb in the future tense.

Just History?

To me, it's a mystery —
Why do people think
Dr. King is just history?
He <u>stand</u> on the brink
of a change. He <u>dream</u>
of equality. He <u>speak</u>
with calm strength. His world <u>seem</u>
cold, but he <u>seek</u>
to warm it. Dr. King, we will remember
you.

____

____

____

____

____

____

____

____

CA **LC 1.3** Identify and use regular and irregular **verbs**, adverbs, prepositions, and coordinating conjunctions in writing and speaking.

Name ______________________________

1. Please read the following journal entry:

i did it i can't believe i finally hit the ball with the bat after weeks of swinging and missing, i finally feel like a baseball player are you as surprised as i am

2. Rewrite this entry using proper capitalization and punctuation. Remember, every sentence starts with a capital letter and every sentence ends with a period, a question mark, or an exclamation point.

____

____

____

____

____

____

____

____

____

____

____

____

Extra practice: Please try the same exercise with the following entry.

my cat spencer is the smartest cat i have ever known he is also the cutest he always comes running when i call him and we even play fetch with a tin foil ball sometimes every night he sleeps on my feet at the end of my bed

W 1.0 Writing Strategies

Name ____________________

When the letters **c** and **g** are followed by **e**, ***i***, or **y**, they usually have a soft sound. Say the following words aloud.

ceiling	circus	cycle
genius	giant	gyroscope

Circle the word with soft c or *g* and write it on the line.

1. The young people were ______________ their plan would work.

careful   certain   cornered

2. They wanted to work in the ______________.

city   country   crowd

3. They could help people exercise in a ______________.

gymnasium   grade school   gang

4. Or they could give ______________ care to sick pets.

glad   grateful   gentle

5. Maybe they could feed the pets ______________.

cereal   corn   cupcakes

6. They could play with the ______________ while they were not working.

game   goose   gerbil

7. They could make sure the animals were free of ______________.

grease   gags   germs

8. Shelby has been learning to play the ______________.

clarinet   cymbals   castanets

Name ______________________________

cranky	selfish	exasperated
specialty	famished	commotion

Choose a vocabulary word from the list that has the opposite meaning of the word(s) in dark type and makes each sentence true. Write it on the line.

1. Mariel is **happy** because she slept for only four hours last night.

   ____

2. I had only a bag of peanuts for lunch, so I was **stuffed** by the time dinner came. ____________________

3. It would be **generous** not to share your lunch with a hungry friend.

   ____

4. My mom felt **pleased** when I forgot to take out the garbage for the fourth time. ____________________

5. Tyler's dog caused a **peaceful pause** when it escaped and ran through a grocery store. ____________________

Use one of the vocabulary words in a sentence of your own.

6. ____

Name ______________________

When you **make judgments**, you may need to use your personal experience. However, you must also be able to support your judgment with evidence from the story.

Read the tale. Then complete the chart.

Anansi was just sitting down to a delicious dinner. Turtle knocked on Anansi's door and asked Anansi if he could share his meal. Anansi didn't want to share his meal, but he agreed. Then he told Turtle he must wash his hands before eating. Turtle crawled to the stream to wash his hands, but by the time he returned to Anansi's table, his hands were dirty again. Anansi sent Turtle away to wash his hands again. By the time Turtle returned, Anansi had finished the last bite of the meal.

Turtle thanked Anansi for sharing his meal and promised him a meal if he ever came to his house. Anansi went to Turtle's house. Turtle had set the table under water. Anansi filled the pockets of his jacket with rocks so he could stay underwater, but Turtle told him he must remove his jacket to eat. Anansi floated to the surface and could not share Turtle's feast.

Valid Judgment	Evidence
1. Anansi is selfish.	
2. Anansi is clever.	
3. Turtle is polite.	
4. Turtle is clever.	

5. Who do you think is more clever, Anansi or Turtle? Support your response with evidence from the tale.

____

____

Name ______________________________

As you read *Ranita, the Frog Princess,* fill in the Make Judgments Chart.

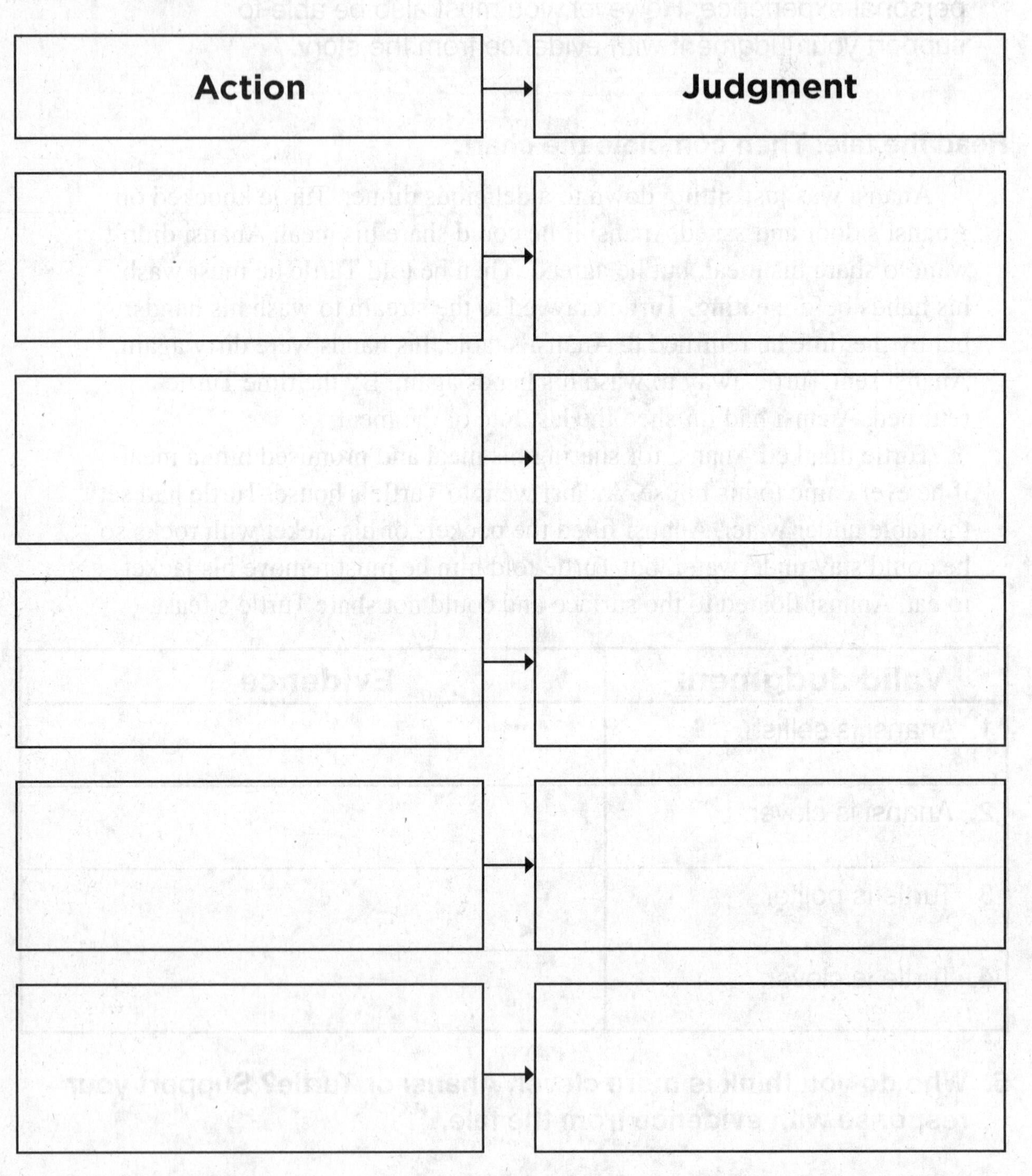

How does the information you wrote in the Make Judgements Chart help you to evaluate *Ranita, the Frog Princess*?

Name ________________________________

As I read, I will pay attention to expression.

	[*Dean Dragon's kitchen. Matthew is struggling to light a*
9	*fire with a match under a cauldron of stew. Dean Dragon*
20	*steps up and lights it with his dragon breath. Priscilla uses*
31	*a large wooden spoon to stir the stew, while Matthew*
41	*starts chopping carrots.*]
44	**Princess Priscilla:** [*inhaling a spoonful of stew with a*
53	*look of pleasure*] Mmm. That smells good already.
61	**Matthew:** Wait until it's finished. It's delicious.
68	**Dean Dragon:** [*smiling*] My vegetable stew is good, if
77	I do say so myself. It's famous among dragons.
86	**Princess Priscilla:** I can see why. [*She smiles at Dean,*
96	*then goes back to stirring the stew.*] I'd just like to get my
109	hands on that Knight Never-Do-Well. He woke me up in
121	the middle of the night and told me that my family was in
134	danger. So of course I came. Then when we got here, he tied
147	me to the tree, told me not to worry, and said he'd be back to
162	rescue me soon. I'd like to take a can opener to that shiny
175	armor of his. 178

Comprehension Check

1. Do you think Knight Never-Do-Well is a reliable person? **Plot Development**

2. Do these characters enjoy working together? Why? **Plot Development**

	Words Read	–	Number of Errors	=	Words Correct Score
First Read		–		=	
Second Read		–		=	

CA **R 1.1** Read narrative and expository text aloud with grade-appropriate fluency and accuracy and with appropriate pacing, intonation, and **expression**.

Practice

Text Feature: Map

Name ______________________________

A **compass rose** shows north, south, east, and west. The **map key**, or **legend**, explains the symbols on the map.

Use the map to answer each question.

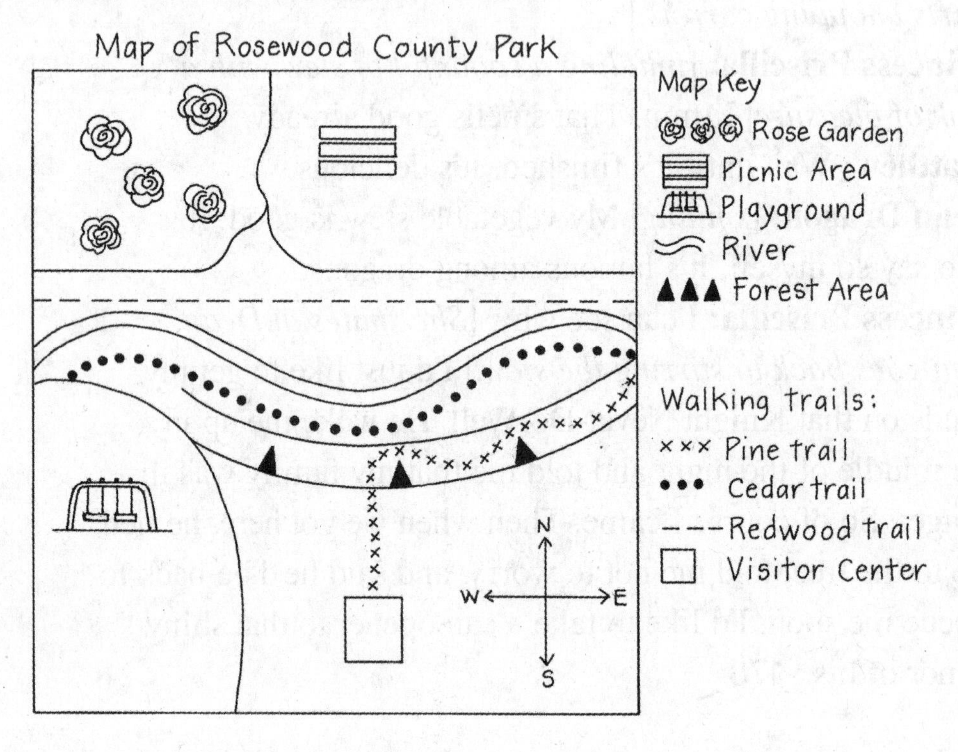

1. The picnic area is to the east of ______________________.

2. Which trail would you take to walk through the forest area?

____

3. Can you take the Cedar trail to get to the Redwood trail? Explain.

____

4. It is possible to get from the Visitor Center to the Rose Garden. What is missing from the map? ______________________

Name ______________________________

Words that have opposite meanings are called **antonyms.** A word can have more than one antonym.

Word	**Antonyms**
glad	*sad, unhappy*
angry	*calm, pleased*

A. Draw lines to match each word in Column 1 with an antonym from Column 2.

Column 1	**Column 2**
1. selfish	**a.** full
2. hungry	**b.** calm
3. noisy	**c.** slow
4. speedy	**d.** unselfish
5. excited	**e.** quiet

B. In the blank, write an antonym for each underlined word.

6. Shayna always remembers ______________ her promises.

7. I felt cheerful ______________ when I woke up.

8. Dad speaks loudly ______________ on the phone.

9. The door slammed ______________ suddenly.

10. The weather outside was sunny ______________.

Name ______________________________

Using the Word Study Steps

1. LOOK at the word.
2. SAY the word aloud.
3. STUDY the letters in the word.
4. WRITE the word.
5. CHECK the word.
   Did you spell the word right?
   If not, go back to step 1.

Find Rhyming Words

Rhyming words have the same ending sounds. Circle the word in each row that has the same ending sounds as the spelling word on the left.

1. **glance**	stance	fence	gleam
2. **spice**	spit	spruce	vice
3. **ounce**	inch	bounce	pound
4. **strange**	arrange	stingy	garage
5. **center**	blender	renter	cement
6. **wedge**	pledge	welt	trudge
7. **sponge**	stage	spare	grunge
8. **bridge**	brought	ridge	ride
9. **germs**	grim	terms	times
10. **scene**	queen	dunce	race
11. **certain**	crept	captain	curtain

CA **LC 1.7** Spell correctly roots, inflections, suffixes and prefixes, and syllable constructions.

Name ______________________________

A. Proofreading

There are six spelling mistakes in the story below. Circle the misspelled words. Write the words correctly on the lines below.

Ana read an article in the newspaper about a fire at a house in a nearby vilage. No one was hurt, but the family lost all of their belongings. Many people were helping them out, but the children didn't have clothes and books for school.

She thought about how strang it would be to lose her own stuff. She was sertain she could find a way to help out. Ana decided to arranje a way for them to get the things they needed.

She started asking people to help. She started with her parents. They gave her a few dollars. Then she asked her grandparents. They gave a little, too. Then she asked her teacher, and next her neighbors. Pretty soon, she had the courage to ask everyone—the polise and even the clowns at the local sircus. When she collected enough money, her dad drove her to the store. She bought new clothes, books, and school supplies. She even bought some new toys. Then she loaded her purchases in a big box and got ready to drop them off to their new owners.

1. ____________ 3. ____________ 5. ____________

2. ____________ 4. ____________ 6. ____________

B. Writing Activity

Imagine that you read about a family who needs help in your town. What might it be? How could you follow Ana's example and do something to fix it? Use at least three spelling words in your paragraph.

____

____

____

____

CA **LC 1.7** Spell correctly roots, inflections, suffixes and prefixes, and syllable constructions.

Practice

Grammar: Main and Helping Verbs

Name ______________________________

- The **main verb** in a sentence shows what the subject does or is.
- A **helping verb** helps the main verb show an action or make a statement.
- ***Have, has,*** and ***had*** can be helping verbs.
- ***Is, are, am, was, were,*** and ***will*** can be helping verbs.

Write a main verb or helping verb to complete each sentence.

1. Charlie ______________ searched for a place to volunteer.
2. He has ______________ lists of groups.
3. Charlie ______________ worrying about choosing the right place to help.
4. He ______________ visit different groups.
5. The people in the soup kitchen are ______________ vegetables.
6. Many people ______________ donated clothes to this group.
7. This afternoon Charlie is ______________ for people who couldn't leave their homes.
8. He has ______________ floors at the animal shelter.
9. Charlie ______________ pitch in wherever he can.
10. The leaders of the groups are ______________ him and telling him he's done a great job.

CA **LC 1.3** Identify and use regular and irregular **verbs**, adverbs, prepositions, and coordinating conjunctions in writing and speaking.

Name ______________________________

- The **main verb** in a sentence shows what the subject does or is.
- A **helping verb** helps the main verb show an action or make a statement. Add ***-ed*** to most verbs to show past tense.
- ***Have***, ***has***, and ***had*** can be helping verbs.
- ***Is***, ***are***, ***am***, ***was***, ***were***, and ***will*** can be helping verbs.

Rewrite the paragraphs below. Be sure to correct any main verbs, helping verbs, or contractions that are used incorrectly.

Everyone should volunteering to help others. It does'nt matter what you do. Any way you can help will makes a difference. You don'ot have to give up all of your free time. You can help even by volunteering just a few hours a week. Many local organizations are count on volunteers.

One way you can help is by working at a soup kitchen. Starting on Wednesday, I will work at the soup kitchen on Fifth Street. I'm look forward to it.

If you take time to help others, you will knowed that you has made your community a better place.

____

____

____

____

____

____

____

____

____

CA **LC 1.3** Identify and use regular and irregular **verbs**, adverbs, prepositions, and coordinating conjunctions in writing and speaking.

Name ____________________

Writing Rubric			
4 Excellent	3 Good	2 Fair	1 Unsatisfactory
Ideas and Content/ Genre	Ideas and Content/ Genre	Ideas and Content/ Genre	Ideas and Content/ Genre
Organization and Focus	Organization and Focus	Organization and Focus	Organization and Focus
Sentence Structure/ Fluency	Sentence Structure/ Fluency	Sentence Structure/ Fluency	Sentence Structure/ Fluency
Conventions	Conventions	Conventions	Conventions
Word Choice	Word Choice	Word Choice	Word Choice
Voice	Voice	Voice	Voice
Presentation	Presentation	Presentation	Presentation

Name ________________________________

Plurals are formed in the following ways:

- Most plural nouns end in ***-s***.
- When a word ends in ***-s, -ss, -sh, -ch***, or ***-x, -es*** is added.
- When a word ends in a **vowel** + ***y, -s*** is added.
- When a word ends in a **consonant** + ***y***, the ***y*** is dropped and ***-ies*** is added.

Write the correct plural form of the underlined word on the line.

1. Many talented artist ________________ have lived and worked in California.
2. Many of them study in city ________________ such as Los Angeles and San Francisco.
3. The artist Ansel Adams took many photo ________________ of the state.
4. His work showed high mountains and lush valley ________________.
5. The state is home to many famous writer ________________, too.
6. The writer Gary Soto writes about his childhood hopes and wish ________________.
7. He writes story ________________ about his family.
8. Soto turns his memory ________________ into art.

Name ______________________________

dismiss	interact	motivate
conceived	definition	

A. From each pair of words below, circle the word that best completes the sentence. Then write the correct word on the line provided.

1. What is the (definition/interact) of the word *genius*? ______________
2. Hearing the music of Louis Armstrong might (dismiss/motivate) you to play the trumpet. ______________
3. When he played, Armstrong liked to (interact/motivate) with the people who watched him. ______________
4. My sister and I (conceived/definition) of a way of playing like Louis Armstrong. ______________
5. Mom will probably (dismiss/interact) our idea of starting a family band. ______________

B. Write new sentences for three of the vocabulary words used above. Underline the vocabulary word in each sentence.

6. ______________________________
7. ______________________________
8. ______________________________

Name ______________________________

A **fact** is a statement that can be proven true.
An **opinion** is a statement that tells someone's feelings or ideas.
It cannot be proven true.
Facts and opinions can appear together.

A. Read the following sentences. After each sentence write *fact* or *opinion*.

1. Our class went on a field trip to the art museum last week.

   ____

2. We saw one painting that was almost 500 years old. ______________

3. It is harder to be a painter than to be a writer. ______________

4. The best painters are from the United States. ______________

5. Some painters study art in college. ______________

6. Going to the art museum is a great way to spend an afternoon.

   ____

B. Write one fact about art. Then write one opinion about art.

7. Fact: ______________________________

8. Opinion: ______________________________

CA **R 2.6** Distinguish between cause and effect and between **fact and opinion** in expository text.

Practice

Comprehension: Fact and Opinion Chart

Name ______________________________

As you read *Words Add Up to Success*, fill in the Fact and Opinion Chart.

Fact	Opinion

How does the information you wrote on this Fact and Opinion Chart help you better understand *Words Add Up to Success*?

CA **R 2.6** Distinguish between cause and effect and between **fact and opinion** in expository text.

Name ______________________________

As I read, I will pay attention to accuracy.

	Thousands of years ago in China, people made an
9	important discovery. They found out that caterpillars of
17	one kind of moth spin cocoons of silk. And better yet, they
29	found out that the cocoons could be unwound and the silk
40	thread could be woven into fabric.
46	Silk fabric is shiny. It is soft and smooth to the touch.
58	It is very light in weight. And it can be dyed in many
71	colors.
72	For thousands of years, the Chinese were the only
81	people who knew how to produce silk cloth. People in
91	other countries wanted to trade for the precious silk
100	fabric. Traders traveled to and from China on one
109	main road. They traded goods such as spices, glass,
118	and gold for silk. Sometimes they even traded horses
127	for silk. Over time, this route became known as the Silk
138	Road. 139

Comprehension Check

1. Are the statements in the second paragraph facts or opinions? **Relevant Facts and Details**

2. What is the main idea of the third paragraph? **Main Idea and Details**

	Words Read	–	Number of Errors	=	Words Correct Score
First Read		–		=	
Second Read		–		=	

R 1.1 Read narrative and expository text aloud with grade-appropriate fluency and accuracy and with appropriate pacing, intonation, and expression.

Name ______________________________

The **Internet** is a collection of computer networks. A **search engine** reviews that collection to help you find information.

To use a search engine:

- Type a key word or a phrase in the Search box.
- The search engine will come back with a list of Web pages that contain the key words.
- When choosing a Web page, select trustworthy sources.

Use the Web page to answer the questions.

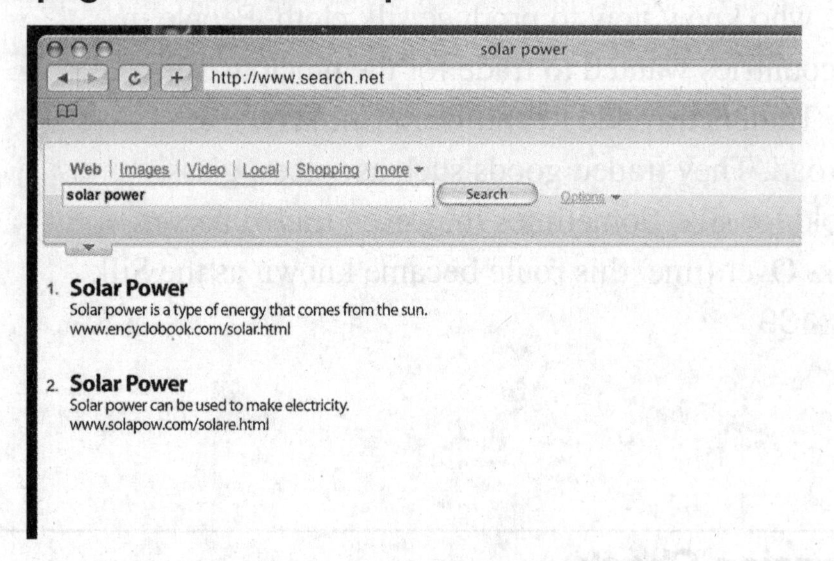

1. What words have been entered in the search box? ______________________________

2. If you clicked on the first Web page listed, what information would you find? ______________________________

3. If you wanted to find information about solar power in California, what words would you put in the search box? ______________________________

4. If you entered the word "California" in the search box, what information would you find? ______________________________

CA **W 1.7** Use various reference materials (e.g., dictionary, thesaurus, card catalog, encyclopedia, online information) as an aid to writing.

Name ______________________________

Cause/Effect Writing Frame

Summarize "Words Add Up to Success."
Use the Cause/Effect Writing Frame below.

Jaime Escalanate's students were in trouble. They were in trouble **because** ____
______________________________.

This **caused** Jaime Escalante to ______________________________.

He **also** ______________________________.

In addition, he ______________________________.

As a result of Jaime Escalante's efforts, ______________________________.

Rewrite the completed summary on another sheet of paper. Keep it as a model for writing a summary of an article or selection using this text structure.

Name ______________________________

A **prefix** is a word part that is added to the beginning of a word to change its meaning. Many prefixes come from **Latin**. Understanding prefixes can help you figure out the meaning of a word.

Prefix	**Meaning**
pre-	before
sub-	under
un-	not

Read each sentence. Write the meaning of each boldface word on the line provided. Use the clues in the table above.

1. When Spencer turned three, he started **preschool**.

____

____

2. The **submarine** traveled to the bottom of the ocean.

____

3. His face is **unforgettable**. ______________________________

4. We rode the **subway** train in New York City.

____

5. We went to a **preview** of the new movie.

____

6. A new bike would be nice to have, but it is **unnecessary**.

____

CA **R 1.4** Know common roots and affixes derived from Geek and Latin and use this knowledge to analyze the meaning of complex words (e.g., *international*).

Name ______________________________

Using the Word Study Steps

1. LOOK at the word.
2. SAY the word aloud.
3. STUDY the letters in the word.
4. WRITE the word.
5. CHECK the word.
   Did you spell the word right?
   If not, go back to step 1.

Word Endings

A. Write the spelling words by adding -es.

1. moss ____________
2. arch ____________
3. dress ____________
4. glass ____________
5. couch ____________
6. patch ____________
7. ranch ____________

B. Write the spelling words by adding -s.

8. cave ____________
9. clam ____________
10. arrow ____________
11. engine ____________
12. mistake ____________
13. prop ____________
14. parent ____________
15. mint ____________

C. Write the spelling words by changing the *y* to *i* and adding -es.

16. baby ____________
17. army ____________
18. supply ____________
19. hobby ____________
20. enemy ____________

LC 1.7 Spell correctly roots, inflections, suffixes and prefixes, and syllable constructions.

Name ______________________________

A. Proofreading Activity

There are six spelling mistakes in the story below. Circle the misspelled words. Write the words correctly on the lines below.

At night, we'd sleep in the tipis. We made our beds by gathering moses. They were really soft. Our blankets were bison hides, which the hunters had shot with arrowes. They also had to use bows and arrows to protect our tribe from enemys.

The Plains was a beautiful place, with wide horizons and rolling hills. Later, it would be made into ranchs with cows and cowboys. But before that, there were no fences, just grass as far as you could see.

Indians were good parentes. They cared very much for their babyes. Mothers would carry them around on their backs and sing to them. The women wore dresses made of deer hides.

1. ______________ 3. ______________ 5. ______________

2. ______________ 4. ______________ 6. ______________

B. Writing Activity

Imagine that you could live on the Plains with an Indian tribe. Write a paragraph describing what you would do. Use at least four spelling words in your paragraph.

____

____

____

____

____

____

____

CA LC 1.7 Spell correctly roots, inflections, suffixes and prefixes, and syllable constructions.

Name ______________________________

- A **linking verb** does not show action. It connects the subject to the rest of the sentence.
- ***Is***, ***are***, ***am***, ***was***, and ***were*** are often used as linking verbs.
- Some linking verbs link the subject to a noun in the predicate.
- Some linking verbs link the subject to an adjective in the predicate.

Complete each sentence by writing the correct linking verb on the line. Then underline the complete subject of the sentence.

1. Our social studies project __________ an interesting assignment.

2. I __________ eager to get started on it.

3. The Pawnee tribe __________ the subject of my project.

4. Mystic Horse __________ my favorite book last year.

5. The Pawnee Indians __________ unfamiliar to me before I read that book.

6. They __________ a group I want to learn more about now.

7. The state of Nebraska __________ the place the Pawnee lived long ago.

8. Many books about the Pawnee __________ located in the school library.

9. The library __________ so big that I can't always find what I need.

10. Our librarian, Ms. Kribble, __________ helpful to students.

Name ______________________________

- A **linking verb** does not show action. It connects the subject to the rest of the sentence.
- ***Is***, ***are***, ***am***, ***was***, and ***were*** are often used as linking verbs.
- Some linking verbs link the subject to a noun in the predicate.
- Some linking verbs link the subject to an adjective in the predicate.

Rewrite the lines of this play. Correct any linking verbs that are used incorrectly. Be sure to use proper punctuation for a play.

T.J. "I need an idea for my social studies project. I can't think of anything."
T.J. paces the room nervously.
CARA *confidently.* "My project are about Pawnee folktales."
T.J. "That's a good idea, Cara." *CARA opens the book and points to a picture.*
CARA. "The Plains tribes is very interesting to read about."
T.J. *excitedly*. "This were a great idea."

____

____

____

____

____

____

____

____

____

____

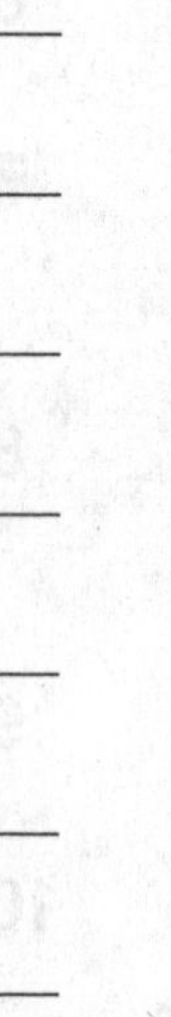

Name ____________________

1. Read the following journal entry:

We walked into the cafeteria with its deafening sounds of kids' shouting. As we sat down, I immediately wrinkled my nose at the sour smell of sauerkraut. The floor beneath my table was slippery with it. My first bite of pizza tasted like socks.

2. Look at the chart below. Each of your 5 senses is listed across the top, and under each heading is a sensory detail from the journal entry above that goes along with each sense.

Setting: Cafeteria

Sound	Smell	Sight	Touch	Taste
deafening shouting	sour sauerkraut	sauerkraut on the floor	slippery sauerkraut	pizza tasted like socks

3. Using the charts below, try to think of sensory details that you might be able to write about to describe the settings listed. Remember, sensory details are descriptions of sight, taste, touch, hearing, and smell.

Setting: Birthday Party

Sound	Smell	Sight	Touch	Taste

Setting: Library

Sound	Smell	Sight	Touch	Taste

4. Now try it with a setting of your choice.

Setting:

Sound	Smell	Sight	Touch	Taste

Extra Practice: Try again using another setting of your choice.

Setting:

Sound	Smell	Sight	Touch	Taste

Name ______________________________

A **compound word** is made up of two short words. The two words together make a new word with a new meaning.

When I was at camp this summer, we built a campfire to keep warm at night.

camp* + *fire* = *campfire
***camp*:** an outdoor place with tents or cabins
***fire*:** the flame, heat, and light given off when wood burns
***campfire*:** an outdoor fire for cooking or keeping warm in a camp

Draw a line dividing the two words that make up the compound word in each sentence. Then write the letter that matches the meaning of each word.

1. We had a bad snowstorm.	___ and ___	a. long, thin rope
		b. coming into being
2. Bentley loved snowflakes.	___ and ___	c. small, thin, flat pieces
3. Hail is made from raindrops.	___ and ___	d. plants with many long, thin leaves
4. The child took the towels off the clothesline when the hail came.	___ and ___	e. white crystals of ice
		f. what people wear
5. The child's birthday was in January.	___ and ___	g. windy, unsettled weather
		h. water from clouds
6. The grasshopper hid during the storm.	___ and ___	i. twenty-four hours
		j. small balls of something
		k. someone or something that jumps

CA R 1.0 Word Analysis, Fluency, and Systematic Vocabulary Development

Name ______________________________

strutting	swarms	barbecue
skyscrapers	glorious	collage

A. Answer each question, substituting the vocabulary word for its underlined definition.

1. Have you seen Jason? Why was he walking in a proud manner down the hall?

____

2. Why were there great numbers of people at the mall?

____

3. What kinds of food do you like to eat at an outdoor gathering at which meat is roasted over an open fire and served?

____

4. Where can you go to see very tall buildings?

____

5. What materials are you using to make that artistic composition made by pasting or gluing materials together on a surface?

____

B. Use two of the words above in one sentence.

6. ______________________________

Name ______________________________

Characters are the people, and sometimes animals, that you read about in a story. The main character is the story's most important character. Pay attention to the things characters say, do, and feel to compare how they change throughout the story.

Read the following passage. Then answer the questions that follow.

Brian said to his mom, "I'm worried about going to art camp. I won't know anyone there."

"Don't worry about it," his mom said. "You'll see. It'll be fine."

When Brian walked into the camp meeting room, he swallowed hard. Most of the tables were full of kids talking and laughing with each other. There was only one spot open, and it was at a table way in the back.

There were three other kids at the table—Alex, Kenya, and Mike. They all knew each other, but they were happy to talk to Brian, too. Brian no longer felt nervous. By the time he went home, he knew he had a new set of friends for the summer.

1. Who is the main character? ____________________

2. Name the other characters in the story.

____

3. What kind of person is Brian in the beginning of the story? ____________

____

____

4. How did Brian change at the end of the story? ____________

____

____

Name ______________________________

As you read *Me and Uncle Romie*, fill in the Setting Flow Chart.

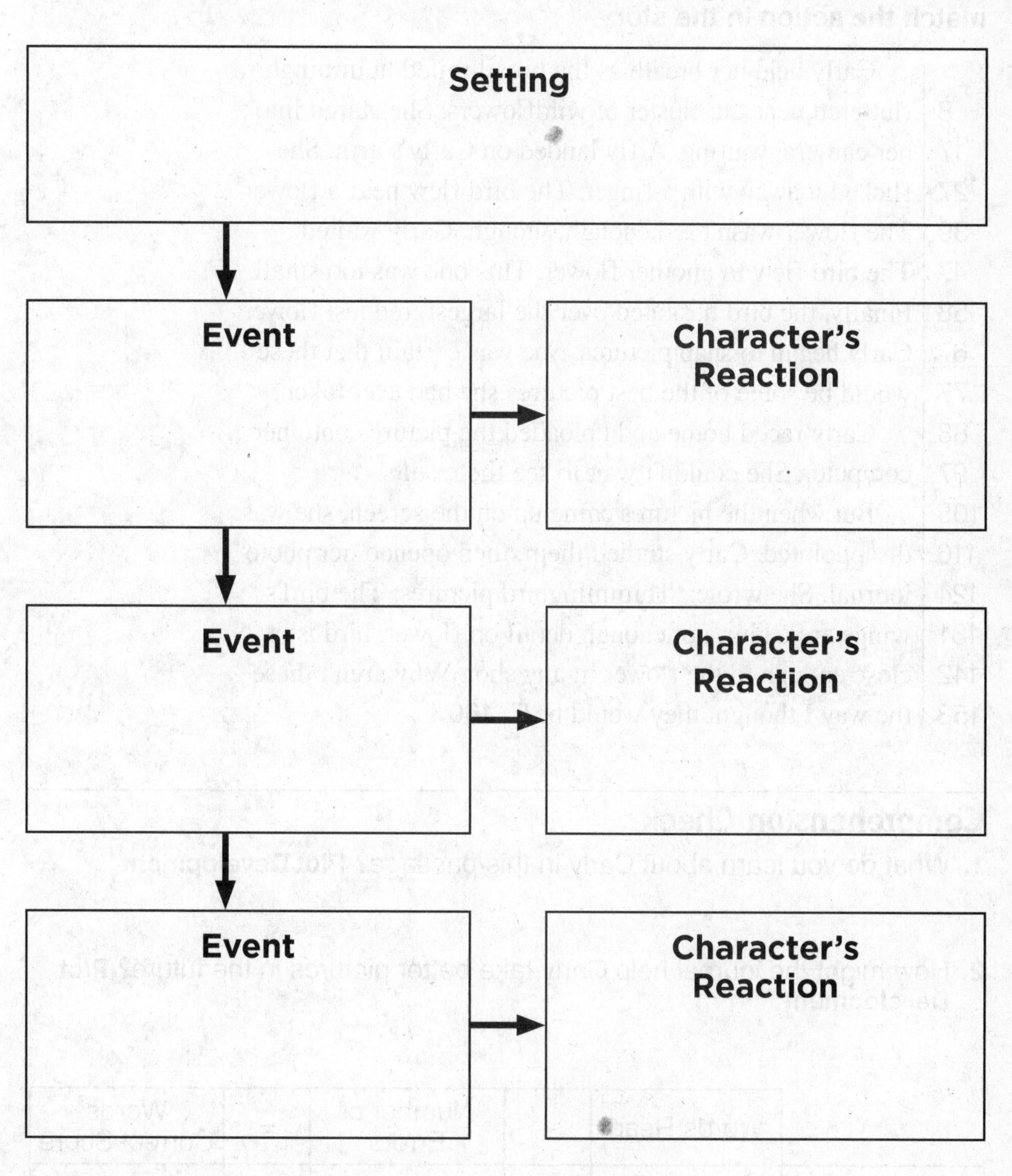

How does the information you wrote in the Setting Flow Chart help you monitor your comprehension of *Me and Uncle Romie*?

Name ____

As I read, I will pay attention to my pacing in order to match the action in the story.

	Carly held her breath as the broad-tailed hummingbird
8	fluttered near the cluster of wildflowers. She stared into
17	her camera, waiting. A fly landed on Carly's arm. She
27	flicked it away with a finger. The bird flew near a flower.
39	The flower wasn't red enough, though. Carly waited.
47	The bird flew to another flower. This one was too small.
58	Finally, the bird hesitated over the largest, reddest flower.
67	Carly began to snap pictures. She was certain that these
77	would be some of the best pictures she had ever taken.
88	Carly raced home and uploaded the pictures onto her
97	computer. She couldn't wait to see the results.
105	But when the pictures came up on the screen, she was
116	disappointed. Carly studied them, then opened her photo
124	journal. She wrote: "Hummingbird pictures: The bird's
131	wings are a blur, not enough detail on flower, bird isn't
142	close enough to the flower in any shot. Why aren't these
153	the way I thought they would be?" 160

Comprehension Check

1. What do you learn about Carly in this passage? **Plot Development**

2. How might the journal help Carly take better pictures in the future? **Plot Development**

	Words Read	–	Number of Errors	=	Words Correct Score
First Read		–		=	
Second Read		–		=	

R 1.1 Read narrative and expository text aloud with grade-appropriate pacing, intonation, and expression.

Name ______________________________

Directions explain how to do something. Sometimes numbered steps are given to tell the reader the order in which things should be done. **Sequence words**, such as ***first*, *then*, *next***, and ***last***, can also help readers follow directions. Sometimes a list of needed **materials** is included in the directions.

Read the following directions. Then answer the questions.

How to Paint a Room

Materials

paint	drop cloth	paint stirrer	roller
painter's tape	paintbrushes	paint tray	

Directions

1. Put drop cloths on the floor and furniture to protect them.
2. Place blue painter's tape around the areas that you do not want painted, like windows, for instance.
3. Open the paint cans and mix the paint with a stirrer.
4. Pour the paint into a paint tray. Use a roller to paint the walls.
5. Use a paintbrush to paint the corners, edges, and other spots the roller can't reach.
6. When you are finished, wash the brushes and rollers with warm water.

1. How many materials are needed to paint a room? ____
2. What is the first thing you should do before you paint a room?

____

3. What do you pour the paint into? ______________________________
4. What would happen if you skipped Step 2?

____

Name ______________________________

Practice

Vocabulary Strategy: Description

Context clues can help readers determine the meaning of an unfamiliar word. Sometimes writers use **description** to help readers define unfamiliar words.

Underline the context clues that describe the meaning of the boldfaced word. Then write the word's definition.

1. We decided that the **theme** of our collage would be what we did during our vacation.

   Definition: ______________________________

2. The chef felt her masterpiece was not complete until she **shredded** cheese into tiny strips and sprinkled it on top of the omelette.

   Definition: ______________________________

3. The young artist worked with many different **mediums**—oil and acrylic paints, colored pencils, and chalk.

   Definition: ______________________________

4. My neighbor offered me the **proposition** of getting $20 each time it snows for shoveling his stairs and sidewalk.

   Definition: ______________________________

5. My two uncles are starting a business together as **joint** owners.

   Definition: ______________________________

6. After we paid our **admission,** we could enter the museum and stay as long as we wished.

   Definition: ______________________________

Name ______________________________

Using the Word Study Steps

1. LOOK at the word.
2. SAY the word aloud.
3. STUDY the letters in the word.
4. WRITE the word.
5. CHECK the word.
Did you spell the word right?
If not, go back to step 1.

Bits and Pieces

Join the first word on the left with a second word on the right that completes each compound spelling word.

1. rail ______________ top
2. fish ______________ line
3. back ______________ speaker
4. desk ______________ room
5. snow ______________ fold
6. clothes ______________ head
7. blind ______________ bowl
8. loud ______________ yard
9. bed ______________ road
10. over ______________ storm
11. new ______________ take
12. your ______________ fire
13. look ______________ case
14. book ______________ spread
15. grand ______________ born
16. over ______________ self
17. bed ______________ parent
18. water ______________ proof
19. under ______________ out
20. camp ______________ do

CA **LC 1.7** Spell correctly roots, inflections, suffixes and prefixes, and syllable constructions.

Name ____________________

A. Proofreading

There are six spelling mistakes in the story below. Circle the misspelled words. Write the words correctly on the lines below.

With his desk top microscope, Jack could see the beauty of snowflakes. They were tiny but had intricate designs. Each one was different, and they were all spectacular.

But Jack was sad because he knew that most people could not see the beauty of snowflakes. They did not have a microscope. It was like they had a blind fold on. So, he decided to under take a new project to let them see for themselves. For a long time, he was on the look out for a camera that could photograph snowflakes, but there was none. He'd have to make it himself.

He read a book case full of books about cameras and started putting one together. It took many tries, but when he finished his camera, he could take pictures of snowflakes and say to anyone he met, "See for your self how beautiful snowflakes are."

1. ____________ 3. ____________ 5. ____________

2. ____________ 4. ____________ 6. ____________

B. Writing Activity

Jack's favorite thing about the snow is snowflakes. Write a letter to a friend describing your perfect day in the snow. Include four spelling words in your writing.

____

____

____

____

____

____

CA LC 1.7 Spell correctly roots, inflections, suffixes and prefixes, and syllable constructions.

Name ______________________________

- Some **irregular verbs** have special spellings when used with the helping verbs ***have, has,*** or ***had***.

Read each sentence and the verb choices in parentheses. Underline the verb choice that correctly completes the sentence.

1. Alice has (did, done) many drawings and photographs of the park in winter.
2. She had (make, made) it a hobby by the time she was ten years old.
3. For the past four years, her parents have (given, gave) her a photo album each year for her birthday.
4. Alice has carefully (put, putted) all of her winter pictures in the albums.
5. Today, the surface of the pond has (frozen, froze).
6. Alice took pictures of the tree because she had (saw, seen) icicles on it.
7. She has (lay, laid) her camera aside while she gets more film out of her bag.
8. By the end of the afternoon, the icicles have (shrunk, shrank) in the sun.
9. Before she went home, Alice had (taken, took) more than 40 pictures.
10. The next morning, she saw that more snow had (fell, fallen).

Name ______________________________

- An **irregular verb** is a verb that does not add ***-ed*** to form the past tense.
- Some irregular verbs have special spellings when used with the helping verbs ***have, has,*** or ***had***.

Rewrite the character sketch below. Be sure to correct any mistakes in the use of irregular verbs.

Margaret

Margaret getted up early this morning. She bringed her camera to the pond. She taked a picture of a fish before it swimmed away. She photographed geese as they fly south for the winter. Soon she had took dozens of pictures.

Ever since she was a little girl, Margaret had know she wanted to be a photographer. By the age of 15, she had winned three photography awards. Now 30 years old, she has write a guide for beginning photographers. She has maked photography her life's work.

____

____

____

____

____

____

____

____

____

____

CA **LC 1.3** Identify and use regular and **irregular verbs**, adverbs, prepositions, and coordinating conjunctions in writing and speaking.

Name ______________________________

1. Please read the following sentence:

When I poured the milk, it was really gross.

2. Now, using your senses, write 2-3 sentences that SHOW what exactly was gross about the milk. If it helps, you can make a list of your 5 senses first.

Example: The milk came out in yellow chunks. (sight)

____

____

____

____

____

____

____

____

____

____

____

____

____

____

____

____

____

Extra Practice: Try the same exercise again using the following sentence.

The tropical bird room at the zoo was very interesting.

Name ______________________________

When you add ***-ed*** or ***-ing*** to a word, sometimes you have to add or drop a letter before adding the ending.

- If the word has a short vowel sound and ends in a single consonant, double the last letter before adding the ending.
- If the word ends in **e**, drop the **e** before adding the ending.

A. Complete the table by writing the correct *-ed* and *-ing* forms of each of these words.

Base Word	Word + *ing*	Word + *ed*
1. hop	______	______
2. hope	______	______
3. flip	______	______
4. force	______	______
5. tap	______	______
6. tape	______	______

B. Write four sentences, each using one of the words above.

7. ______________________________

8. ______________________________

9. ______________________________

10. ______________________________

Name ______________________________

eavesdropping	route	logical
jumble	scornfully	acquaintance

Answer the questions using a vocabulary word that means the same as the underlined word or phrase.

1. Did the raccoon leave a big mess when it turned over the garbage can?

____

2. Is this the most direct way to get to the lake?

____

3. Was the owl in the tree listening in on your conversation by the campfire?

____

4. Is it reasonable to expect an animal to act like a person?

____

5. Would a mouse be the not-too-close friend of a cat in real life?

____

6. Would an owl look at a wolf with dislike and disrespect?

____

Name ______________________________

A **theme** is the subject, or topic, that an author is writing about. To identify a story's message, ask yourself, "What is the subject of this story?"

Read the passage. As you read, think about the theme. Then answer the questions that follow.

Mario Mouse did not always do as he was told. His mother had told him never to leave the safety of their mouse hole, because the world outside was dangerous. But Mario was an adventurous mouse. One evening he ran out of the hole to see the world.

My, the world was big! He found himself in a huge room. It had chairs, a couch, and low tables. In one corner, he saw a big box that had bright pictures and spoke! Mario crept forward to look at the bright pictures.

Just then, a big furry animal bounded into the room, making snarling noises. Mario was terrified. He let out a squeak and scurried back to his mouse hole. He dove through it, back to safety. "Mom was so right," he thought.

1. What is one of the themes of this story? ______________________________

____

____

2. On the lines below, list three story events that support the theme that you identified.

a. ______________________________

b. ______________________________

c. ______________________________

Name ______________________________________

As you read *The Cricket in Times Square*, fill in the Theme Map.

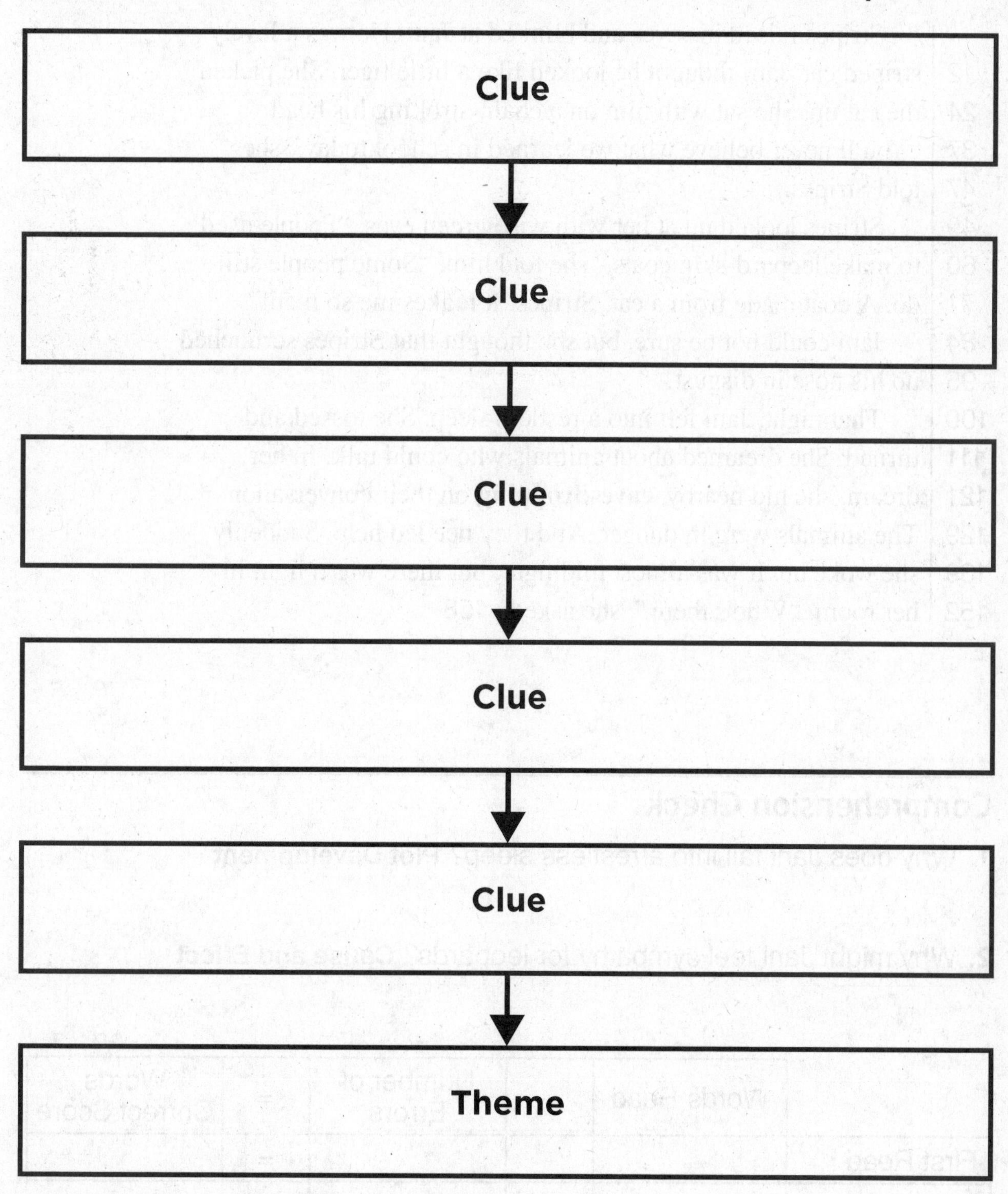

How does the information you wrote in the Theme Map help you to better understand *The Cricket in Times Square*?

Name ____________________

As I read, I will pay attention to expression.

Stripes raised his eyes and blinked at Jani. He was a lovely
12 striped cat. Jani thought he looked like a little tiger. She picked
24 the cat up. She sat with him on a chair, stroking his head.
37 "You'll never believe what we learned in school today," she
47 told Stripes.
49 Stripes looked up at her with wise green eyes. "People used
60 to make leopard-skin coats," she told him. "Some people still
71 do. A coat made from a cat, Stripes. It makes me so mad!"
84 Jani could not be sure, but she thought that Stripes scrunched
95 up his nose in disgust.
100 That night, Jani fell into a restless sleep. She tossed and
111 turned. She dreamed about animals who could talk. In her
121 dream, she hid nearby, **eavesdropping** on their conversation.
129 The animals were in danger. And they needed help. Suddenly
139 she woke up. It was almost midnight, but there was a light in
152 her room. "Who's there?" she asked. 158

Comprehension Check

1. Why does Jani fall into a restless sleep? **Plot Development**

2. Why might Jani feel sympathy for leopards? **Cause and Effect**

	Words Read	–	Number of Errors	=	Words Correct Score
First Read		–		=	
Second Read		–		=	

CA **R 1.1** Read narrative and expository text aloud with grade-appropriate fluency and accuracy and with appropriate pacing, intonation, and expression.

Name ______________________________

Advertisements use pictures and text to get people to buy or do something. Advertisements use several techniques of persuasion:

- loaded language, such as *best*, *better*, and *special*
- bandwagon, or urging that you join many other people
- testimonials, or the backing of a celebrity
- warnings that the offer is good for a limited time only

Read each advertisement. Then answer the questions.

Our world-class bird feeder will blow you away! It's the best there is. As Bob Wells of the Nature Channel says, "You won't find a better feeder anywhere."

1. What techniques does the advertisement use? ______________________

2. What words or phrases did you use to figure out the advertisement's approach? ______________________

Join your friends and neighbors by donating to the Save the Tigers fund. Act now and receive this beautiful tote bag.

3. What techniques does the advertisement use? ______________________

4. What words or phrases did you use to figure out the advertisement's approach? ______________________

Name ______________________________

Context clues are words in the same or surrounding sentences that help a reader figure out the meaning of an unfamiliar word.

Read the passage below. Then write the meaning of each word in dark type and the context clues that helped you figure it out.

The **audience streamed** into the theater to hear Regina Jackson's talk. Hundreds of people moved smoothly but quickly into their seats. Jackson was the world's leading **authority** on **jaguars**. No one else knew more than she did about the lives of these big cats. From the moment she began to speak, everyone sat quietly. You could see by their interested expressions that they were **fascinated** by what she had to say. When Regina finished, everyone stood up and began to applaud.

1. **audience** Definition: ______________________________

   Context clues: ______________________________

2. **streamed** Definition: ______________________________

   Context clues: ______________________________

3. **authority** Definition: ______________________________

   Context clues: ______________________________

4. **jaguars** Definition: ______________________________

   Context clues: ______________________________

5. **fascinated** Definition: ______________________________

   Context clues: ______________________________

Name ____________________

Using the Word Study Steps

1. LOOK at the word.
2. SAY the word aloud.
3. STUDY the letters in the word.
4. WRITE the word.
5. CHECK the word.
   Did you spell the word right?
   If not, go back to step 1.

Word Endings

Write the spelling word by crossing off the final -e and then adding the ending *-ed*.

1. save ____________
2. force ____________
3. taste ____________
4. scare ____________

Write the spelling word by crossing off the final -e and then adding the ending *-ing*.

5. save ____________
6. force ____________
7. taste ____________
8. scare ____________

Write the spelling word by doubling the final consonant and adding the ending *-ed*.

9. rip ____________
10. skip ____________
11. flip ____________
12. tap ____________
13. flag ____________

Write the spelling word by doubling the final consonant and adding the ending *-ing*.

14. rip ____________
15. skip ____________
16. flip ____________
17. tap ____________
18. flag ____________

Write the spelling word by adding the ending *-ed*.

19. discuss ____________

Write the spelling word by adding the ending *-ing*.

20. discuss ____________

CA **LC 1.7** Spell correctly roots, inflections, suffixes and prefixes, and syllable constructions.

Practice

Spelling: Inflectional Endings

Name ________________________________

A. Proofreading

There are six spelling mistakes in these paragraphs. Circle the misspelled words. Write the words correctly on the lines below.

My father was fliping through the paper when he saw the following ad:

"Do you have a caring home? Do you love scipping alongside your best friend? You are in luck! There are dozens of puppies at the local shelter just waiting to be savd."

My dad rippd the ad out of the paper to show my mother. They discused the pros and cons of getting a dog for a long time. Finally they told me their decision. I nearly flipd with excitement. That afternoon we drove to the animal shelter and picked out our very own puppy!

1. ____________ 3. ____________ 5. ____________

2. ____________ 4. ____________ 6. ____________

B. Writing Activity

Write about your favorite animal. Use at least three spelling words in your paragraph.

____

____

____

____

____

____

____

____

CA LC 1.7 Spell correctly roots, inflections, suffixes and prefixes, and syllable constructions.

- A **pronoun** is a word that takes the place of one or more nouns.
- A pronoun must match the noun it refers to.
- Singular pronouns are *I*, *you*, *he*, *she*, *it*, *me*, *him*, and *her*.
- Plural pronouns are *we*, *you*, *they*, *us*, and *them*.

Write the pronoun that correctly replaces the underlined noun in each sentence.

1. At first, Roy didn't want to go to the nursing home because Roy thought the place was boring. ____________
2. Mrs. Allen said Mrs. Allen found out that dogs were allowed in the nursing home. ____________
3. Roy knew Grandpa would be happy to see Buddy, so Roy decided to bring Buddy. ____________
4. The receptionist at the nursing home said to Roy, "I see Roy brought a friend today." ____________
5. Mrs. Allen said, "Mrs. Allen got Buddy's medical records this morning." ____________
6. Grandpa said, "I'm glad you brought Buddy to Grandpa." ____________
7. Grandpa asked Martha if Buddy was allowed in the nursing home. ____________
8. Another man saw Buddy and said he had a dog that looked like Buddy. ____________
9. You can treat high blood pressure if you take medicine for the problem. ____________
10. Roy threw the ball to Buddy so Buddy could fetch it. ____________

Name ______________________________

- A **pronoun** is a word that takes the place of one or more nouns.
- A pronoun must match the noun it refers to.
- Singular pronouns are *I*, *you*, *he*, *she*, *it*, *me*, *him*, and *her*.
- The pronoun *I* must always be capitalized.
- Plural pronouns are *we*, *you*, *they*, *us*, and *them*.

Read the following paragraphs. Circle all the incorrect pronouns. Then rewrite the paragraph, making sure all pronouns are correct and match their nouns.

Yesterday i went to the store to buy some food for my dog, Jones. Mr. Edwards greeted her when I came through the door.

She said, "What can me do for you, Sheila?"

"I need six cans of the Beef and Chicken Special Diet."

Mr. Edwards added up the prices and said, "The total is $11.37."

"Me am sorry," I said. "My mother only gave I $10. How much is it if me only buy four cans?"

"Let's see. It would be $9.25," he said.

"All right. That solves my problem. She'll only buy four."

____

____

____

____

____

____

____

____

Name ______________________

1. Please read the following: Think about what the two characters are feeling.

Marcus wanted a turn on the swing. Kim was hogging it.

2. Rewrite this sentence as a dialogue that SHOWS me what Kim and Marcus are feeling. For example:

"Come on Kim, I have waited forever for the swing," yelled Marcus, but Kim just ignored him.

____

____

____

3. Rewrite these sentences as a dialogue that shows what the characters are feeling. Each person talks at least two times.

a. Billy was really hungry. Mandy ate the last two cookies.

b. Charlotte was bored at the store. Sara was not finished shopping.

____

____

____

____

Extra Practice: Rewrite the following sentence as a dialogue as you did above.

Mom was in a hurry to leave. Davey could not find his other shoe.

____

____

____

____

____

Name ______________________________

When words end in a consonant + ***y***, you do two things to add endings like ***-er*** or ***-ed***. First you change the ***y*** to ***i***. Then you add the ending.

A. Change *y* to *i* and add the indicated ending to each word. Then write the new word in the blank.

lazy + er **1.** ______________

reply + ed **2.** ______________

worry + es **3.** ______________

happy + est **4.** ______________

empty + er **5.** ______________

family + es **6.** ______________

dizzy + est **7.** ______________

funny + er **8.** ______________

B. Follow the model and write four more words.

9. ______________ ______________

10. ______________ ______________

11. ______________ ______________

12. ______________ ______________

Name ______________________________

territory	investigates	solitary
prehistoric	nutrients	communication

Read each sentence and decide whether it is true or false. If it is true, write True. If it is false, write False, and explain why.

1. An ant *investigates* new discoveries of food with its antennae.

____

2. Ants guard the *territory* in which they live.

____

3. Ants are not *prehistoric* creatures because they've been around for only about 500 years.

____

4. Some insects are *solitary*, which means they like living in groups.

____

5. Like ants, we get our *nutrients* from the foods we eat.

____

6. Ants use *communication* to tell each other where to find food.

____

Name ______________________________

Writers use **relevant facts and details** to give their readers a description of a topic. Descriptions help readers better understand the topic.

Read the passage. Then answer the questions that follow.

The Life Cycle of the Ant

Egg

Ants begin life as tiny white or yellowish eggs. The eggs are oval in shape and less than 1/16 of an inch long. They hatch in two to six weeks.

Larva

Larvae look like small white worms. They don't have legs, and they can't move much. They grow for several weeks to several months. Larvae shed their skin over and over as they grow.

Pupa

During this stage, the ants change into their adult bodies. In the end, they look like white ants. Their legs and antennae are snug against their bodies. After this stage, they are full-grown.

1. Give two descriptions from the passage that relate to the topic.

____

____

2. Why does the author include the description that the eggs are 1/16 of an inch long? ______________________________

____

Name ______________________________

As you read *The Life and Times of the Ant*, fill in the Description Webs.

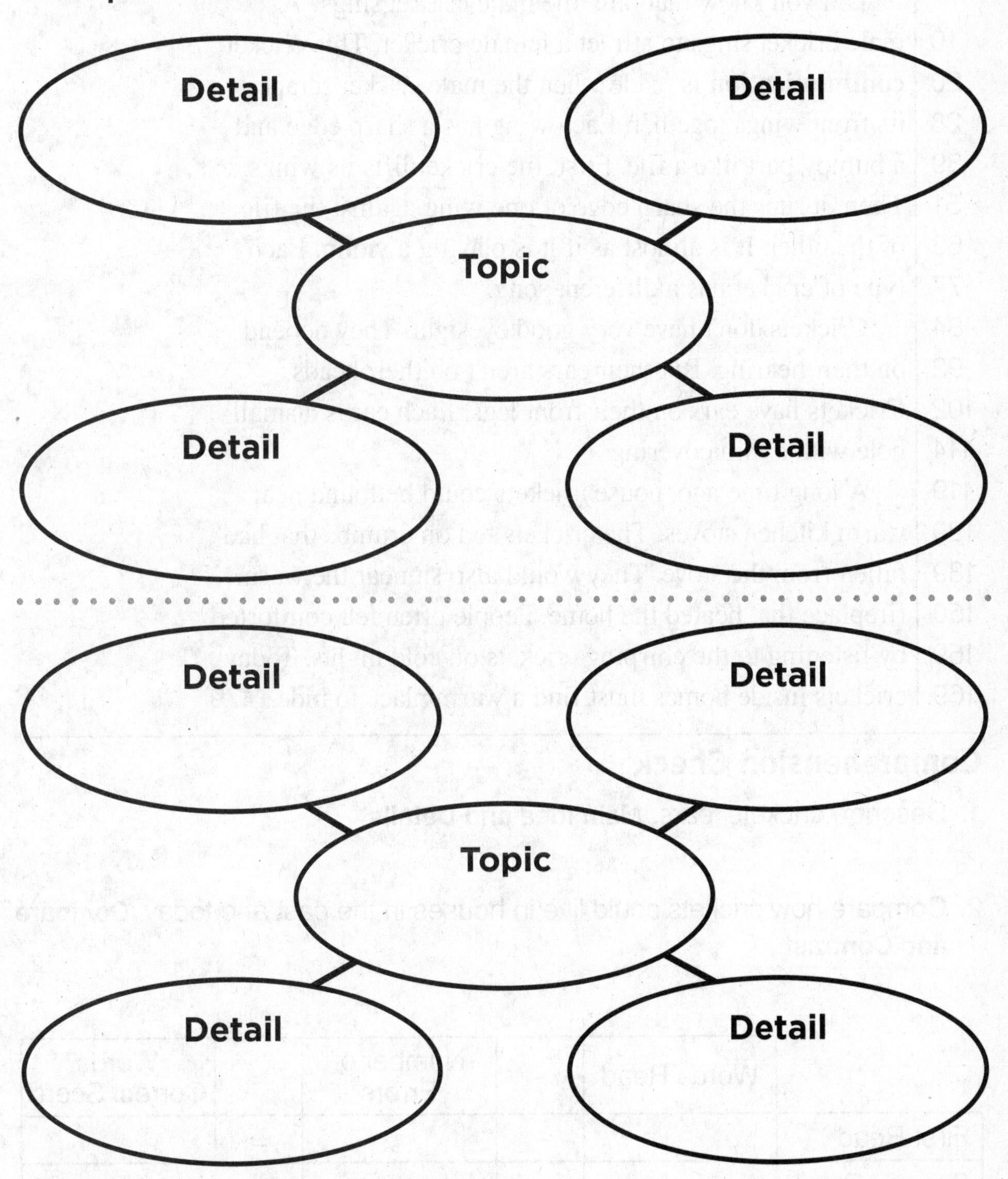

How does completing the Description Webs help you analyze the text structure of *The Life and Times of the Ant*?

Name ______________________________

As I read, I will pay attention to pacing.

Did you know that only the male cricket sings? A
10 male cricket sings to attract a female cricket. This cricket
20 **communication** is made when the male cricket scrapes
28 its front wings together. Each wing has a sharp edge and
39 a bumpy part like a file. First, the cricket lifts its wings.
51 Then, it rubs the sharp edge of one wing against the file
63 of the other. It is almost as if it is playing a violin. Each
77 type of cricket has a different song.
84 Crickets don't have very good eyesight. They depend
92 on their hearing. But their ears aren't on their heads.
102 Crickets have ears on their front legs. Each ear is a small
114 hole with a thin covering.
119 A long time ago, house crickets could be found near
129 warm kitchen stoves. The crickets fed on crumbs that had
139 fallen from the stove. They would also sit near the warm
150 fireplace that heated the home. People often felt comforted
159 by listening to the chirping crickets on cold nights. Today
169 crickets inside homes must find a warm place to hide. 179

Comprehension Check

1. Describe crickets' ears. **Main Idea and Details**

2. Compare how crickets could live in houses in the past and today. **Compare and Contrast**

	Words Read	–	Number of Errors	=	Words Correct Score
First Read		–		=	
Second Read		–		=	

CA **R 1.1** Read narrative and expository text aloud with grade-appropriate fluency and accuracy and with appropriate pacing, intonation, and expression.

Name ______________________________

A **fable** is a short story that teaches a lesson, or **moral**. Fables often have animal **characters** that behave like people. The **plot** of a fable or other story is what happens in the story.

Read each fable and answer the questions.

A fire ant fell into a river and started to panic. A dove saw this happen, plucked a leaf from a tree, and dropped it near the ant. The ant climbed on the leaf and got safely to shore. "Thank you," said the ant. "I wish I could repay you for your help." The dove waved her wing and flew away. Soon after, a hunter came by and aimed at the dove. The ant ran up to the hunter and stung him on the foot. The hunter missed his target.

1. Why do you think the ant helps the dove?

____

____

2. What might the moral of this fable be?

____

A crow was very thirsty. He found a pitcher and tried to drink from it but couldn't reach the water. Then he started dropping pebbles into the pitcher. With each pebble the water rose higher until, at last, it rose high enough for him to drink.

3. What is the most important event in the story?

____

____

4. What do you think the moral of this story is?

____

Name ______________________________

Many English words came from other languages. Some words came from Greek, the language of Greece. Knowing the meaning of **Greek roots** can help you understand other words that use the same root.

Column 1	**Column 2**
dino- = terrible	*-logy* = the study of
astro- = star	*-scope* = see
tele- = far	*-saur* = lizard
bio- = life	*-naut* = sailor

Match a Greek root from Column 1 with one from Column 2 to get the English word described. Then use the word in a sentence.

1. star sailor ____________________

____

2. see far ____________________

____

3. terrible lizard ____________________

____

4. the study of life ____________________

____

CA **R 1.4** Know common roots and affixes derived from Greek and Latin and use this knowledge to analyze the meaning of complex words (e.g., international).

Name ______________________________

Using the Word Study Steps

1. LOOK at the word.
2. SAY the word aloud.
3. STUDY the letters in the word.
4. WRITE the word.
5. CHECK the word.
   Did you spell the word right?
   If not, go back to step 1.

Find and Circle

H	A	P	P	I	E	S	T	Q	F	F	M
S	F	R	X	Z	R	O	V	V	M	U	E
F	D	E	C	P	E	R	Q	Z	J	N	R
L	I	T	O	E	P	R	G	B	C	N	R
E	Z	T	Z	N	L	I	B	J	A	I	I
A	Z	I	I	N	I	E	A	U	R	E	E
S	I	L	L	I	E	S	T	M	R	R	R
I	E	Y	Y	E	D	T	L	P	I	W	L
L	S	P	W	S	V	A	R	I	E	D	C
Y	T	F	A	M	I	L	I	E	S	Q	Z
P	W	E	M	P	T	I	E	R	U	Y	W
W	O	R	R	I	E	D	O	G	G	Y	B
M	A	R	R	I	E	S	D	R	B	M	R

CA LC 1.7 Spell correctly roots, inflections, suffixes and prefixes, and syllable constructions.

A. Proofreading

There are five spelling mistakes in this paragraph. Circle the misspelled words. Write the words correctly on the lines below.

Not only is Catherine my best friend, but she is also one of the sillyest people I know. She is marrier than any of the merriest elves in the North Pole. When Catherine comes over, she thinks up the best games to play. Once we built a giant city made only out of penies. It was so funny. It was even funier when she pretended to be a giant monster and knocked all the pennies down. We have the best time together. Some people might feel sorry for Catherine because she is blind. They might think she cannot do all the things she loves to do. But Catherine and I think that is silly. We both know Catherine is one of the happyest kids in our class.

1. ______________ **3.** ______________ **5.** ______________

2. ______________ **4.** ______________

B. Writing Activity

Write about your best friend. Use at least three spelling words in your paragraph.

____

____

____

____

____

____

____

____

CA **LC 1.7** Spell correctly roots, inflections, suffixes and prefixes, and syllable constructions.

Name ____________________

- Use a **reflexive pronoun** instead of an object pronoun if the subject of the sentence is doing the action to himself or herself.
- *Myself*, *yourself*, *himself*, *herself*, *itself*, *ourselves*, and *yourselves* are reflexive pronouns.

Fill in the blanks in the sentences below with the correct reflexive pronoun.

1. Be careful and don't hurt __________.
2. After I go swimming, I dry __________ with a towel.
3. Your baby sister can't feed __________.
4. He made __________ dizzy by spinning around and around.
5. Let's give __________ a break and try again later.
6. The bird washed __________ in the puddle.
7. Boys, please get __________ ready for dinner.
8. The gardener shut the door and locked __________ in the shed.
9. My grandfather almost fell, but he caught __________.
10. Look at __________! You're covered in mud!
11. I tried to reach the towel __________.
12. He looked at __________ in the mirror.
13. We can plant that tree __________.
14. My sister cannot feed __________ without some help.
15. You can help __________ to some cookies.

Name ______________________

- Use a **subject pronoun** as the subject of a sentence.
- *I*, *you*, *he*, *she*, *it*, *we*, and *they* are subject pronouns.
- Use an **object pronoun** after an action verb or after a word such as *for*, *at*, *of*, *with*, or *to*.
- *Me*, *you*, *him*, *her*, *it*, *us*, and *them* are object pronouns.

A. Rewrite the paragraphs below. Circle every pronoun that is not used correctly.

Someone gave I directions to the museum

You and me need to walk to Maple Street. Then turn right at Oak Street. Mr. Exeter lives there. Him and me go on walks sometimes. If him is in his yard, he will give a big wave to you and I.

When we got to the museum, we saw Mrs. Peters. Her and my dad went to school together. Them often like the same paintings

B. Rewrite the passage above. Use the correct forms of the pronouns. Be sure to use capital letters and end punctuation correctly.

____

____

____

____

____

____

____

____

____

1. Please read the following: Think about what could be happening.

"Look at that!"

2. Now add details to show what is happening. For example:

"Look at that," shouted Larry as he stepped backwards.

____

____

3. Now complete this dialogue by making sentences that SHOW what is happening and who is speaking. You need to add characters and specific verbs and details to SHOW what they are doing.

"Look at that!"

"What do you think it is?"

"I don't know, but look at it."

"I've never seen anything like it."

____

____

____

Extra Practice: Repeat this drill with the following dialogue:

"Can you see where you are going?"

"No. Can you?"

"No. Oh, gross – I just stepped on something slimy!"

"Let's get out of here!"

____

____

____

____

Name ____________________

- Words like ***spool***, ***grew***, ***move***, ***soup***, and ***suit*** have the **/ü/** sound.
- Words like ***brooks*** and ***should*** have the **/u̇/** sound.
- Words like ***cubes*** and ***mule*** have the **/ū/** sound.

Notice that ***oo*** and ***ou*** can stand for different sounds. Remember which sound they stand for in each word you learn.

Read the words in the box. Then put each word under the correct heading.

would	knew	books	food
dune	looking	wood	prove
you'll	scoop	used	cute

/ü/	/u̇/	/ū/
____________	____________	____________
____________	____________	____________
____________	____________	____________
____________	____________	____________
____________	____________	____________
____________	____________	____________

CA R 1.0 Word Analysis, Fluency, and Systematic Vocabulary Development

Name ______________________________

calculates donor community linked restore

Write the vocabulary word that completes each sentence on the line.

1. Some people in our ______________ are planning a beach clean-up day.

2. They plan to ______________ the beach to the way it was 100 years ago.

3. The group leader ______________ that the group will need $1,200 to clean up the beach.

4. One ______________ gave $500.00 to our clean-up group.

5. Groups all over our state are ______________ together to help save our beaches.

Practice

Name ____________________

Comprehension: Fact and Opinion

A **fact** is a statement that can be proven true.
An **opinion** is a statement that tells someone's ideas or feelings. It cannot be proven true or false.
Words such as ***I think, the best,*** or ***should*** signal opinions.
When you read, ask yourself: *Can this statement be proven?*

Read the passage.

Many young people enjoy building houses with blocks. But some are going a step further. They are helping to build homes. Many states have organizations that help build houses for families who need them. Some groups build new houses; other groups fix up old houses. Volunteers of all ages work together on these projects. Some jobs for kids include painting and building toolboxes. I think that everyone should volunteer for a building group.

1. Write one opinion from the passage.

____

____

2. Write the clue words that tell you this is an opinion.

____

3. Write one fact from the passage.

____

____

4. What sources could you use to check this fact?

____

CA **R 2.6** Distinguish between cause and effect and between **fact and opinion** in expository text.

Name ___________________________

As you read *Writing on the Wall*, fill in the Fact and Opinion Chart.

Fact	Opinion

How does the information you wrote on this Fact and Opinion Chart help you better understand *Writing on the Wall*?

R 2.6 Distinguish between cause and effect and between **fact and opinion** in expository text.

Name ______________________________

Practice

Fluency: Accuracy

As I read, I will pay attention to my accuracy.

	You may know people who like to talk about
9	themselves. Marie Curie was not that kind of person. She
19	went about her work quietly and cautiously. She didn't
28	brag about what she did, although she could have. She was
39	a woman of great wisdom. Marie Curie made discoveries
48	that changed the world.
52	Marie Curie's work opened up a new field of medicine
62	called radiology. Her experiments led to better ways of
71	treating people with cancer and other diseases.
78	She was the first woman ever to win a Nobel Prize.
89	This is a special prize given each year to people who do
101	important work. Years later, Marie won a second Nobel
110	Prize. She was the first person ever to do so.
120	Marie Curie lived at a time when few women were able
131	to be scientists. She was born poor and was often ill. Yet
143	she rose above all that to become a hero to the world. 155

Comprehension Check

1. What happened as a result of Marie Curie's hard work? **Cause and Effect**

2. What kind of person was Marie Curie? **Relevant Facts and Details**

	Words Read	–	Number of Errors	=	Words Correct Score
First Read		–		=	
Second Read		–		=	

R 1.1 Read narrative and expository text aloud with grade-appropriate fluency and accuracy and with appropriate pacing, intonation, and expression.

Name ______________________________

When you **skim,** you look quickly through a selection to find out what it is about. You look for its main idea and important details.

When you **scan,** you run your eyes through a text looking for a specific word or phrase. You don't read every word.

Read the information below. Then answer the questions that follow.

How to Scan for Information

When you scan for information, follow these steps.

- Identify the key words and phrases that you are looking for.
- Pass your eyes over each line of print quickly.
- Don't stop until you see your key word or phrase.
- Double-check to be sure that you have found the information.

1. Why would it not have been useful to skim the passage in the box?

____

____

____

2. If you're looking for key words and phrases, are you skimming or scanning? ____________

3. Which of the following is the best key word or phrase that you would use for scanning?

a. The Great Wall **b.** murals **c.** painting

4. Which do you think is more useful, skimming or scanning? Explain your answer. ______________________________

____

CA **R 2.2** Use appropriate strategies when reading for different purposes (e.g., full comprehensions, location of information, personal enjoyment).

Name ______________________________

Practice

Comprehension: Writing Frame

Description Writing Frame

Summarize *Writing on the Wall*.
Use the Description Writing Frame below.

The Great Wall of Los Angeles is the longest mural in the world. There are **many interesting facts** about this famous piece of art.

One interesting fact is ______________________________
____
______________________________.

A second interesting fact is ______________________________
____
______________________________.

A third interesting fact is ______________________________
____
______________________________.

A fourth interesting fact is ______________________________
____
______________________________.

The Great Wall helps bring all people from the community together.

Rewrite the completed summary on another sheet of paper. Keep it as a model for writing a summary of an article or selection using this text structure.

CA R 2.0 Reading Comprehension

Name ______________________________

The **origin** of a word is the word's history.
Knowing a word's origin can help you understand its meaning.

echo *noun.* a sound that repeats. *word origin:* from Echo, a character in a Greek myth who was made to repeat the last words anyone said to her

pajamas *noun.* loose-fitting pants and shirt worn for sleeping. *word origin:* from a Persian word meaning "leg clothing"

piano *noun.* musical instrument with a keyboard. *word origin*: from an Italian word meaning "soft and loud"

sofa *noun.* a soft seat for more than one person. *word origin:* from a Turkish word meaning "bench"

Read the definitions, then answer the questions.

1. How does knowing the history of the word *echo* help you understand the word? ______________________________

____

2. How does knowing the history of the word *pajamas* help you understand the word? ______________________________

____

3. How does knowing the history of the word *piano* help you understand the word? ______________________________

____

4. How does knowing the history of the word *sofa* help you understand the word? ______________________________

____

CA **R 1.2** Apply knowledge of **word origins**, derivations, synonyms, antonyms, and idioms to determine the meaning of words and phrases.

Name ______________________________

Practice

Spelling: /ü/, /ū/, and /u̇/ Sounds

Using the Word Study Steps

1. LOOK at the word.
2. SAY the word aloud.
3. STUDY the letters in the word.
4. WRITE the word.
5. CHECK the word.
   Did you spell the word right?
   If not, go back to step 1.

Find and Circle

Where are the spelling words?

X	Z	T	U	N	E	S	T	O	O	L	Z
C	R	E	W	X	C	G	S	E	E	W	O
O	J	K	P	W	D	Q	Y	Z	X	C	O
O	T	P	F	O	O	D	O	M	S	Y	M
K	B	W	S	X	V	B	U	O	N	R	W
I	R	M	O	V	E	G	'	O	H	S	P
E	O	T	S	H	O	U	L	D	U	P	S
V	O	X	W	Q	U	S	L	R	G	O	T
Y	K	V	X	Z	W	E	P	M	E	O	O
K	S	U	I	T	S	D	F	G	J	L	O
S	T	E	W	I	N	G	R	O	U	P	P
P	G	R	E	W	W	O	O	L	Z	X	Q

CA LC 1.7 Spell correctly roots, inflections, suffixes and prefixes, and syllable constructions.

Name ______________________________

Practice

Spelling: /ü/, /ū/, and /u̇/ Sounds

A. Proofreading Activity

There are six spelling mistakes in this paragraph. Circle the misspelled words. Write the words correctly on the lines below.

People have yewsed a lot of energy over the years. We use gasoline to make our cars moove. We use electricity to cook our fud. We use oil to heat our homes. It's about time we started looking for some new sources of energy! Many people believe we shuld try to use the energy of the sun and wind. In Denmark, they use hoog windmills to collect energy from wind. In Japan, a groop of builders make homes with tiles on the roof that absorb the heat of the sun. If we work together, we can find solutions to our energy problems.

1. ____________ **3.** ____________ **5.** ____________

2. ____________ **4.** ____________ **6.** ____________

B. Writing Activity

Write about ways that you can help save energy. Use at least three spelling words in your paragraph.

____

____

____

____

____

____

____

____

____

CA **LC 1.7** Spell correctly roots, inflections, suffixes and prefixes, and syllable constructions.

Name ______________________________

- The verbs ***have*** and ***be*** have special forms in the present tense.

Have		**Be**	
I have	We have	I am	We are
You have	You have	You are	You are
He/She/It has	They have	He/She/It is	They are

Write the correct form of the underlined verb to complete each sentence.

1. I has ______________ a way to tell which house is yours.
2. Your house have ______________ six solar panels on its roof.
3. We has ______________ had them since last year.
4. They be ______________ helping us save energy.
5. They has ______________ already saved us some money.
6. I be ______________ trying to get my friends to use solar panels.
7. I think Fred and Elliot be ______________ going to buy some.
8. Bill be ______________ helping protect the environment.
9. Helen are ______________ good with tools.
10. She have ______________ a big truck that she uses on the job.
11. We be ______________ building an addition to our house.
12. Dad have ______________ to nail the beams.
13. We be ______________ putting in two windows.
14. Now you has ______________ a good design.

Name ______________________________

- A **present-tense verb** must agree with its subject pronoun.
- Add **-s** to most action verbs when you use the pronouns ***he, she,*** and ***it***.
- Do not add **-s** to an action verb in the present tense when you use the pronouns ***I, we, you,*** and ***they***.
- The verbs ***have*** and ***be*** have special forms in the present tense.

Rewrite the story. Be sure all verbs agree with their pronouns.

Working on the North Slope

Right now, I is far from my family. I is now working in a place called the North Slope. That is way up in Alaska. I has only been here about a month, but my friends Steve and Rob has been here about two years. We is here to build an oil pipeline. A few years ago, they found oil north of here. Now we is building a pipeline. When it is done, they will be able to put the oil on ships. It will be at least two years before the job are over. I am glad to be working, but I will be happy to see my family again.

____

____

____

____

____

____

____

____

____

CA LC 1.0 Written and Oral English Language Conventions

Name ______________________

Writing Rubric			
4 Excellent	3 Good	2 Fair	1 Unsatisfactory
Ideas and Content/ Genre	Ideas and Content/ Genre	Ideas and Content/ Genre	Ideas and Content/ Genre
Organization and Focus	Organization and Focus	Organization and Focus	Organization and Focus
Sentence Structure/ Fluency	Sentence Structure/ Fluency	Sentence Structure/ Fluency	Sentence Structure/ Fluency
Conventions	Conventions	Conventions	Conventions
Word Choice	Word Choice	Word Choice	Word Choice
Voice	Voice	Voice	Voice
Presentation	Presentation	Presentation	Presentation

Name ________________________________

As I read, I will pay attention to expression.

	The monkey was having a simply splendid day. Then
9	she spotted a tiger bounding toward her through the jungle.
19	The monkey was sure the tiger would eat her on the spot.
31	She had to think fast.
36	The monkey covered a big pile of coconuts with some
46	banana leaves. She marched back and forth in front of it.
57	The tiger was intrigued by the monkey's odd behavior
66	and didn't attack. "What are you doing?" the tiger
75	demanded.
76	"I'm the king's guardian," proclaimed the monkey.
83	"I am guarding the king's food."
89	"Hmm," the tiger thought. "The king's food is bound to
99	be more delicious than that skinny monkey. Perhaps I can
109	trick the monkey into giving it to me."
117	"You are too small to be the king's guardian," said the
128	tiger. "A big animal like me should be the protector of
139	his food." 141

Comprehension Check

1. What is the author's purpose in this passage? **Author's Purpose**

2. What problem does the monkey face? How does she try to solve it? **Problem and Solution**

	Words Read	–	Number of Errors	=	Words Correct Score
First Read		–		=	
Second Read		–		=	

CA **R 1.1** Read narrative and expository text aloud with grade-appropriate fluency and accuracy and with appropriate pacing, intonation, and expression.

Name ______________________________

Technical manuals give multistep instructions that tell you to how to do something or tell you how something works.

Rescue teams at a disaster have to know first aid. They may have read a manual such as the one below to learn the proper first aid for cuts. Read this page from a first-aid manual, then answer the questions that follow.

First Aid for Cuts

1. Stop the bleeding. If bleeding doesn't stop on its own, apply gentle pressure with a clean cloth or bandage. Hold the pressure continuously for 20 to 30 minutes.
2. Clean the wound. Rinse the wound with clear water only. Soap can irritate the wound, so keep it out of the actual wound. Clean the area around the cut with soap and water.
3. Apply antibiotic to the cut. This will help discourage infection.
4. Cover the wound with a bandage to keep the wound clean and speed healing.
5. Change the bandage daily, or whenever it gets wet or dirty.
6. Watch for sign of infection, such as redness, swelling, or warmth.

1. What does this technical manual explain? ______________________________

____

2. What is the first step in the first-aid procedure? ______________________________

3. Why should you not wash the wound with soap? ______________________________

____

4. Why should you cover the wound with a bandage? ______________________________

____

5. What is the last step? ______________________________

Name ______________________

The underlined letters in the following words show you different ways to spell the **/ô/** sound: ***bald***, ***stalk***, ***straw***, ***caught***. Notice that in ***bald*** you pronounce the ***l***, but that in ***stalk*** you do not.

Read the list of words below. Then sort the words into two columns. The left column is for words with the /ô/ sound. The right column is for other words.

laws	catch	malt	bows
sale	wall	band	talking
wail	mall	strawberry	taught

Words with /ô/	**Other Words**
____________	____________
____________	____________
____________	____________
____________	____________
____________	____________
____________	____________
____________	____________
____________	____________

Name ______________________

assembled	assured	headlines
unstable	applauded	hoisting

Write the word that matches each meaning. Then write your answer in the crossword puzzle.

Across

1. built ______________

2. certain ______________

4. not steady ______________

Down

1. clapped to show appreciation for a performance ______________

3. newspaper article titles ______________

Name ______________________________

An **author's perspective** is his or her point of view. It may include the author's attitudes and opinions about a subject. The words *best*, *worst*, *should*, and *ought to* are often used to signal the author's opinion.

Read the paragraph. Then answer the questions.

I was having the worst day. My oral report was due tomorrow and I still couldn't think of how to make it interesting. I didn't want to bore everyone by just reading from note cards. Just then, my little sister Nita came bursting in. "Great!" I thought. "Just what I need—a visit from Nita the Nuisance."

"What's wrong?" Nita asked.

"My report is due tomorrow and I can't think of how to make it more exciting," I explained.

Nita thought for a moment. Then her face lit up. "I'll be right back, Gina," she exclaimed. When she returned, she had a paper bag on each hand. "Let's make puppets for your report," she said. "You can do a puppet show."

"Why didn't I think of that?" I wondered aloud. I gave my little sister a hug and thanked her. "When we get done," I told her, "I will help you practice your soccer drills." I should remember to be more patient with little sisters!

1. How does the author feel about reading an oral report from note cards?

____

2. How does the author feel about her younger sister at the beginning of the story? How do you know? ______________________________

____

3. Does the author think it is important to show appreciation when someone helps you? How do you know? ______________________________

____

4. What word in the sentence *I should remember to be more patient with little sisters* signals an opinion? ______________________________

Name ______________________________

As you read *My Brothers' Flying Machine*, fill in the Author's Perspective Map.

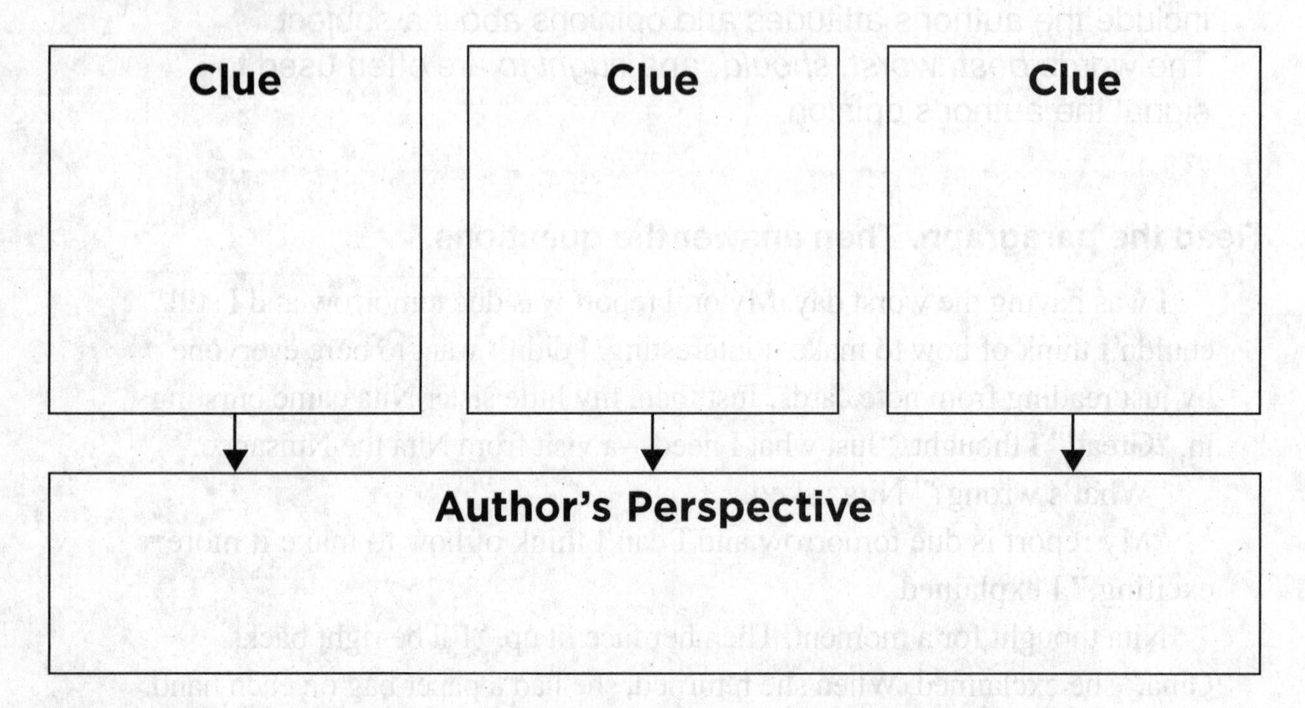

How does the information you wrote in your Author's Perspective Map help you understand the author's feelings and opinions in *My Brothers' Flying Machine*?

Name ______________________________

As I read, I will pay attention to my pacing in order to match the action in the story.

	In 1903, Wilbur and Orville Wright built an airplane with
9	an engine. They became the first people to fly a power-driven
20	aircraft safely. Flight became safer and more popular in the
30	decades after the Wright brothers' first flight. Many people
39	dreamed of becoming pilots. James Banning was one of them.
49	Banning knew that learning to fly was not going to be easy
61	for him because of racial segregation. Blacks and whites usually
71	attended separate schools, ate in separate restaurants, and drank
80	from separate water fountains. There were many people who did
90	not think African Americans should have the opportunity to be
100	pilots. But James Banning was determined.
106	James Banning was born in the territory of Oklahoma in 1899.
116	His parents, like many other formerly enslaved people, had moved
126	there after the Civil War. The Homestead Act allowed them to
137	claim 160 acres of land to farm. They hoped to have better lives
149	far from where they had worked as captives. 157

Comprehension Check

1. What kind of character did James Banning have? **Main Idea and Details**

2. What was the opinion that people held about African American pilots during segregation? **Relevant Facts and Details**

	Words Read	–	Number of Errors	=	Words Correct Score
First Read		–		=	
Second Read		–		=	

CA **R 1.1** Read narrative and expository text aloud with grade-appropriate fluency and accuracy and with appropriate **pacing**, intonation, and expression.

Name ____________________

Repetition is using a word or phrase several times throughout a poem for emphasis.

Personification is a literary device in which animals or things are given human characteristics.

Read the poem. Then answer the questions that follow.

Operation Migration

A new millennium approaches, filled with hope and cheer.
But will it see the whooping crane for many of its years?
A forgotten resolution to migrate and survive
Keeps the birds from knowing the route or how or why.

A pilot has a brainstorm, filled with hope and cheer.
But will it teach the whooping crane to live for many years?
A pilot and a glider would lead the way and show
The whooping cranes that followed where the route is, so they'd know.

The pilot glances back and he's filled with hope and cheer.
Two rows of flapping whooping cranes follow in the rear.
Suspended in the balance between the Earth and sky,
Will the birds remember? Will the birds survive?

Another nest of hatchlings, filled with hope and cheer.
Another brood of whooping cranes to follow late this year.
A pilot in a glider between the Earth and sky.
Each year more birds remember and the whooping crane survives.

1. Which phrases in the poem are examples of repetition?

____

2. What is one example of personification in the poem?

____

CA **R 3.5** Define figurative language (e.g., simile, metaphor, hyperbole, **personification**) and identify its use in literary works.

Name ______________________________

A **suffix** is a word part that can be added to the end of a base word. Adding a suffix to a base word changes its meaning. When added to the end of a verb, the suffix ***-er*** or ***-or*** means "a person who."

teach + *er* = *teacher* (a person who teaches)
act + *or* = *actor* (a person who acts)

Look for the verb. Then add the correct suffix to make a word that means the same as the entire phrase in bold.

1. **A person who travels** in an airplane is a ______________.
2. **A person who invents** a new machine is an ______________.
3. **A person who helps** others is a ______________.
4. **A person who makes** a kite is a kite ______________.
5. **A person who rides** a bicycle is a bicycle ______________.
6. **A person who survives** a crash is a ______________.
7. **A person who explores** a new idea is an ______________.
8. **A person who researches** the history of airplanes is a ______________.

Name ______________________________

Using the Word Study Steps

1. LOOK at the word.
2. SAY the word aloud.
3. STUDY the letters in the word.
4. WRITE the word.
5. CHECK the word.
   Did you spell the word right?
   If not, go back to step 1.

Find and Circle

Where are the spelling words?

S	T	R	A	W	B	E	R	R	Y	L	Z
F	J	K	X	C	A	U	G	H	T	A	M
C	C	A	W	E	Z	D	F	H	P	W	P
V	A	W	Q	F	D	R	A	W	N	S	K
S	L	H	S	A	T	H	O	U	G	H	T
T	L	A	H	L	G	R	J	B	W	B	A
A	E	L	A	S	F	S	Q	U	A	L	L
L	R	T	W	E	X	Q	W	H	L	P	K
K	P	S	L	F	B	Z	Y	A	K	M	I
J	X	V	S	M	A	L	L	L	E	D	N
C	H	A	L	K	L	J	P	F	R	Z	G
S	T	R	A	W	D	F	O	U	G	H	T

CA LC 1.7 Spell correctly roots, inflections, suffixes and prefixes, and syllable constructions.

Name ______________________________

A. Proofreading

There are six spelling mistakes in this paragraph. Circle the misspelled words. Write the words correctly on the lines below.

What If…

Lazily the bawld eagle flew over the water. Looking down, he could see the huge coral reef just below the surface of the waves. Smaul fish darted everywhere. The eagle imagined what it would be like to be a giant shark. All day he would stalck the reefs. Whatever he cought would be his next meal. Just then, a cold breeze ruffled the eagle's feathers. In the air, he could smell that a great sqwall was coming in from the south. "Luckily," the eagle thawt, "I am a bird and not a shark. I can fly away from the rain instead of swimming all day in the water." With that, the eagle flew toward land.

1. ____________ 3. ____________ 5. ____________
2. ____________ 4. ____________ 6. ____________

B. Writing Activity

Write about an animal you might like to be. Use at least three spelling words in your paragraph.

____

____

____

____

____

____

____

CA **LC 1.7** Spell correctly roots, inflections, suffixes and prefixes, and syllable constructions.

Name ______________________________

- *Its*, *their*, and *your* are possessive pronouns.
- *It's*, *they're*, and *you're* are contractions for *it is*, *they are*, and *you are*.
- The word *there* means "in that place." It sounds just like *their* and *they're*.

Write the homophone that correctly completes each sentence.

1. their they're there

Go to a coral reef and explore the warm, clear waters ____________.

2. Its It's

____________ not uncommon to find corals in many bright colors.

3. their they're there

Corals belong to a family of animals, and ____________ relatives include jellyfish and anemones.

4. Its It's

____________ even possible to find corals growing on shipwrecks.

5. its it's

A sponge eats by pumping water through tiny holes in ____________ body.

6. their they're there

The bottom of the ocean is a busy place, and many creatures live ____________.

7. your you're

Which one is ____________ favorite: the sea stars, the sand dollars, or the spiny lobsters?

8. their they're there

No matter which one is your favorite, ____________ all important to life under the sea.

Name ________________________________

- *Its*, *their*, and *your* are possessive pronouns.
- *It's*, *they're*, and *you're* are contractions for *it is*, *they are*, and *you are*.
- The word *there* means "in that place." It sounds just like *their* and *they're*.

Rewrite each sentence in the following short essay. There are six homophone mistakes.

Most people care about there environment and do things to protect it. But places exist here and their that we don't see every day. Its important to take care of them, too. This summer I visited a beautiful coral reef. But a coral reef isn't just a nice place to visit. Its also like a neighborhood. It's millions of cracks and holes are home to many kinds of sea creatures. When I visited their, I learned that people have to take care of the oceans, not just the land.

____

____

____

____

____

____

____

____

____

____

Name ____

"I love playing basketball." I said.

"Me too. I could play it all day!" he agreed.

Who taught you that jump shot I asked

Nobody he said I taught myself.

1. Read the dialogue at the top of this page. Add the quotation marks and punctuation to the last two lines. Follow the pattern you see in the first two lines.
    - Put quotation marks around the speaker's words.
    - Start a new line.
    - Indent when the speaker changes.
2. Now practice adding quotation marks and punctuation to the lines below.

Want to play knockout I asked.

You're brave. No one beats me at knockout he laughed.

That's because you never played me before I bragged.

Extra Practice:

I don't think it will fit back in that bag said Dee

Maybe it will if we fold it up really small suggested Carl

No way said Dee. It's twice as big as the bag.

Name ______________________________

A two-syllable word with the **VCCV pattern** is usually divided between the two consonants.

swal low   wel come

The first syllable of a VCCV word is a **closed** syllable. That means it has a short vowel sound and ends in a consonant.

A. Divide each word below into syllables. Write the syllables in the blanks provided.

1. copper __________ __________

2. member __________ __________

3. planner __________ __________

4. market __________ __________

5. summer __________ __________

6. slender __________ __________

7. fossil __________ __________

8. blanket __________ __________

9. fiction __________ __________

10. witness __________ __________

11. litter __________ __________

B. Which syllable is accented in these words?

12. ______________

Name ______________________________

climate	silken	lumbering
lurk	shimmer	eerie

A. Substitute a vocabulary word for the underlined word or words in each sentence.

1. The rattlesnake's rattle makes a scary sound, warning us to keep out of its way. ____________

2. Alligators often lie in wait in the reeds until small animals come near.

____

3. A bear's heavy, awkward step warns small creatures in its path.

____

4. The surfaces of frozen ponds glow brightly in the winter sunlight.

____

5. Cacti are plants adapted to the dry weather in the desert.

____

6. A spider's web is made of soft, smooth strands. ____________

B. Choose three vocabulary words and use them in one sentence.

____

____

____

The **main idea** of a selection tells you what it is all about. The supporting **details** in the selection help you to understand the main idea. The main idea is often, but not always, stated in the first sentence.

Read the passage and answer the questions that follow.

Many newborn rattlesnakes do not survive their first year of life. A baby rattlesnake is only about ten inches long. Although they have short fangs and a poisonous bite, they are often eaten by birds and animals. The adult rattlesnakes do not raise their young. The young snakes are entirely on their own. Many die of hunger. In the winter they die if they do not find a warm place where they can hibernate.

1. What is the main idea of this passage?

____

2. What supporting details tell you how young rattlesnakes are in danger? List two details on the lines below.

____

____

____

3. What supporting detail tells you how baby rattlesnakes can survive in the winter?

____

4. What supporting detail tells you how baby rattlesnakes can attempt to defend themselves?

____

CA **R 3.2** Identify the main events of the plot, their causes, and the influence of each event on future actions.

Name ______________________________

As you read *A Walk in the Desert*, fill in the Main Idea Chart.

Main Idea ______________________________

____

____

Detail 1 ______________________________

____

Detail 2 ______________________________

____

Summary ______________________________

____

____

How does the information you wrote in the Main Idea Chart help you to summarize *A Walk in the Desert*?

CA **R 3.2** Identify the main events of the plot, their causes, and the influence of each event on future actions.

Name ______________________________

As I read, I will pay attention to pacing.

The Sahara is the world's largest desert. It is nearly
10 the size of the United States. The Sahara extends over
20 10 countries in northern Africa. Like all deserts, it gets
29 fewer than 10 inches (24 cm) of rain a year.
37 In parts of the Sahara, you can see nothing but sand for
49 miles. A sand dune forms when wind carries sand over a
60 large rock. The sand drops, and gradually a hill of sand
71 grows.
72 However, about 80 percent of the world's deserts are
80 not sandy. This is true within the Sahara as well. Deserts
91 begin as rock. The rock is worn away and broken apart by
103 wind, rainstorms, and changing temperatures. Over time,
110 the rock is broken into smaller and smaller pieces. The
120 rock breaks down first into boulders, then into stones, and
130 finally into sand. In some places, the Sahara is made up of
142 huge rocks and gravel. 146

Comprehension Check

1. What makes the Sahara a desert? **Main Idea and Details**

2. State the details of how a desert is formed. **Main Idea and Details**

	Words Read	–	Number of Errors	=	Words Correct Score
First Read		–		=	
Second Read		–		=	

CA **R 1.1** Read narrative and expository text aloud with grade-appropriate fluency and accuracy and with appropriate pacing, intonation, and expression.

Name ______________________________

A **flow chart** is a good way to show a process from start to finish. It uses words joined by arrows to show the order of steps.

Look at the flow chart below. Then answer the questions.

The Water Cycle

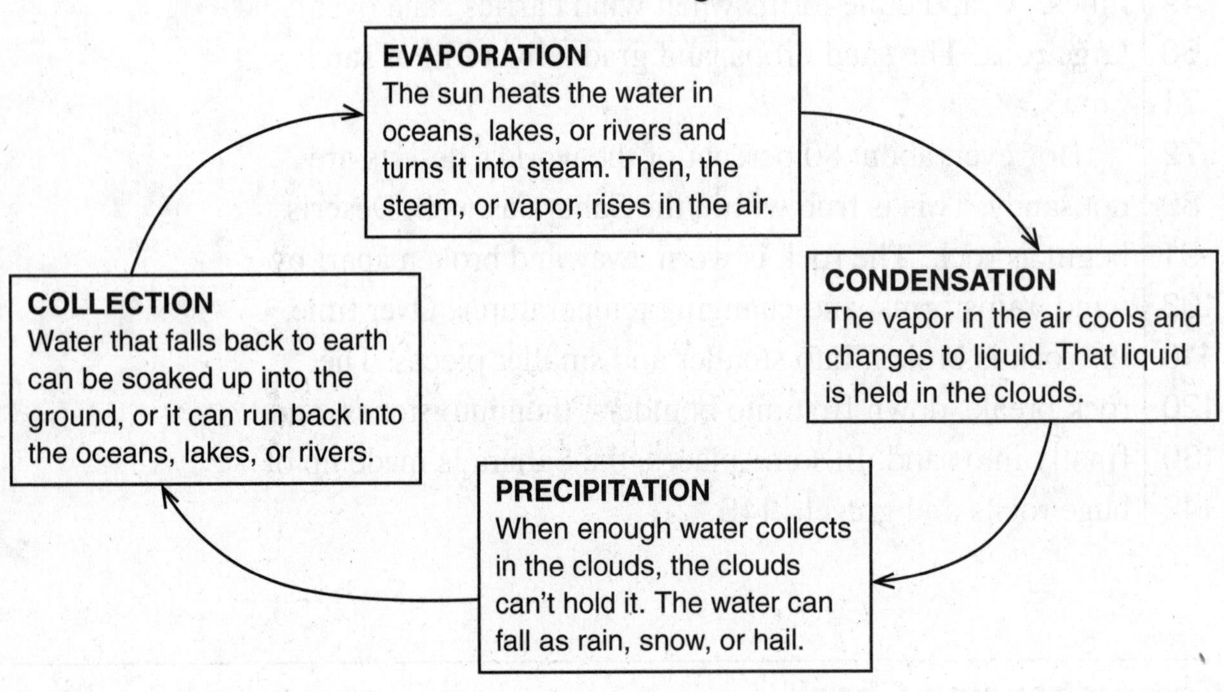

1. What natural process does this flow chart show?

____

2. What happens after collection?

____

3. What happens during condensation?

____

4. What two things can happen to water during collection?

____

Name ______________________________

Sometimes **surrounding words** can provide the context you need to figure out the meaning of an unfamiliar word.

Read the following sentences. Circle the answer that best fits in the blank.

1. A **border** _____ often separates one country from another.
   a. of green flowers **b.** such as a river

2. **Venomous** snakes, _____, kill prey with their poisonous bite.
   a. including rattlesnakes **b.** in the zoo

3. In the West, the open **range** of _____ gradually became fenced in.
   a. empty plains **b.** deep lakes

4. Many desert animals hide from **predators** _____.
   a. like cows **b.** such as foxes

5. At high **elevations** _____ there are fewer trees and plants.
   a. under the ocean **b.** near the top of mountains

6. **Fledglings,** _____, hatch from eggs in the spring.
   a. such as baby wrens **b.** such as full-grown hawks

7. **Nocturnal** animals, _____, look for food between dusk and dawn.
   a. like bats and owls **b.** like whales and dolphins

8. Western farmers plant **orchards** full of _____.
   a. orange and lemon trees **b.** chickens

Name ______________________________

Practice

Spelling: Closed Syllables

Using the Word Study Steps

1. LOOK at the word.
2. SAY the word aloud.
3. STUDY the letters in the word.
4. WRITE the word.
5. CHECK the word.
   Did you spell the word right?
   If not, go back to step 1.

Find and Circle

Find and circle the hidden spelling words.

X	T	H	R	I	L	L	E	R	X	X	Q	W	S
P	I	C	K	E	T	V	Y	P	K	D	P	Q	W
Z	C	N	O	D	D	E	D	L	Y	I	L	Z	A
V	K	V	X	F	K	Y	V	A	Z	P	A	J	L
W	E	L	C	O	M	E	X	N	K	P	S	W	L
I	T	V	Y	S	B	L	A	N	K	E	T	X	O
T	Y	Z	Z	S	U	M	M	E	R	R	I	J	W
N	Y	X	D	I	N	N	E	R	Z	W	C	W	Q
E	W	I	L	L	O	W	Z	X	V	V	X	X	S
S	L	E	N	D	E	R	B	L	O	S	S	O	M
S	W	V	L	A	N	W	F	O	G	G	Y	Z	Q
M	E	M	B	E	R	R	U	M	B	L	E	S	Z

CA **LC 1.7** Spell correctly roots, inflections, suffixes and prefixes, and syllable constructions.

Name ______________________

A. There are six spelling mistakes in this flyer for the library's book club. Circle the misspelled words. Write the words correctly on the lines below.

Wellcom to the Main Street Library! We hope you will join us this somer each Saturday at noon for our book club meeting. When the weather is nice, we meet under the willo tree in front of the library. Bring your lunch and a blanket to sit on while we discuss some wonderful books and stories.

To become a memmbur of the club, all you have to do is show up!

Our first book is a real thriller! It's about a boy who becomes a hero because he is a wittnes to a crime. Next up is a story about a dinosaur fosel that a scientist in Montana found.

We hope to see you this Saturday!

1. ____________ 3. ____________ 5. ____________

2. ____________ 4. ____________ 6. ____________

B. Writing Activity

What can you learn about in the library? Write a paragraph about something you have learned by using the library, or about something you would like to learn. Use at least four spelling words in your description.

____

____

____

____

____

____

CA LC 1.7 Spell correctly roots, inflections, suffixes and prefixes, and syllable constructions.

Name ____________________

- **Proper adjectives** are formed from proper nouns.
- A proper adjective begins with a capital letter.
- **Common adjectives** are not formed from proper nouns. Do not capitalize common adjectives.

On the line, rewrite each proper adjective correctly.

1. Today I sat and read in the herman w. block room at the library.
____
2. I read a book about bears who live in the michigan woods.
____
3. I also learned that mosquitoes live in the florida swamps.
____
4. I read about a chinese custom of having brides wear red at weddings.
____
5. The room had a shelf of books about asian countries.
____
6. This library has more books than both pleasantville libraries put together.
____
7. I won't miss the chill of minnesota winters.
____
8. I lived near the canadian border, where it got very cold.
____
9. That reminds me, I want to find a book on eskimo life.
____
10. I already read a book on native american tribes.
____

Name ______________________________

- **Adjectives** describe nouns or pronouns.
- **Proper adjectives** are formed from proper nouns.
- A proper adjective begins with a capital letter.
- **Common adjectives** are not formed from proper nouns. Do not capitalize common adjectives.

Rewrite each sentence in the paragraph below. Remember to use commas and *and* correctly with adjectives. Capitalize proper adjectives. Use a separate page if you need to.

The little, bookstore on the corner is different from the huge, Smithville bookstore in town. Both stores have lots of interesting, and exciting books. But that's the only way they are alike. The small, blue, store on the corner is warm dim. It is filled with old and, unusual books. This store is not like the big smithville store. The Smithville store is bright, and cool. It has new, books by famous popular writers. There is even a counter where you can get a hot sweet tasty cup of cocoa.

____

____

____

____

____

____

____

____

____

____

Name ______________________________

Drill 1: Putting Events in Logical Order

1. Read:

I was late for school.
My alarm clock never went off.
I jumped out of bed.
I woke up.

2. Write the sentences in an order that makes sense:

1. ______________________________

2. ______________________________

3. ______________________________

4. ______________________________

Name ______________________________

An **open syllable** ends with a long vowel sound. Open first syllables have the **V/CV pattern**.

A **closed syllable** ends with a consonant. The vowel sound is short. Closed first syllables may have the **VC/V pattern**.

Read the words below. Listen for the vowel sound in the first syllable and draw a slash to show where to divide each word. If you have doubts, look up the word in a dictionary. Then, on the line, write whether the first syllable is open or closed.

1. h a b i t ______________
2. n e v e r ______________
3. w i p e r ______________
4. t a l e n t ______________
5. r o b i n ______________
6. m e t e r ______________
7. c i d e r ______________
8. l e v e l ______________
9. p r o m i s e ______________
10. f a m o u s ______________
11. l i m i t ______________
12. f i n i s h ______________

interfere	guardian	awkward
agile	proclaimed	convinced

Use the context clues in each sentence to help you decide which vocabulary word fits best in the blank.

Small Snake couldn't move like the other snakes. "I'm so ________________," he cried.

Caterpillar offered to lend Small Snake a few legs. The young reptile stumbled on them.

Raven stuck out her chest and ________________, "I am the one who can make this poor snake ________________ enough to slither here and there."

Mr. Caterpillar offered to help, but Raven waved him away and said, "Do not ________________ with what I am doing." She was ________________ her way was best.

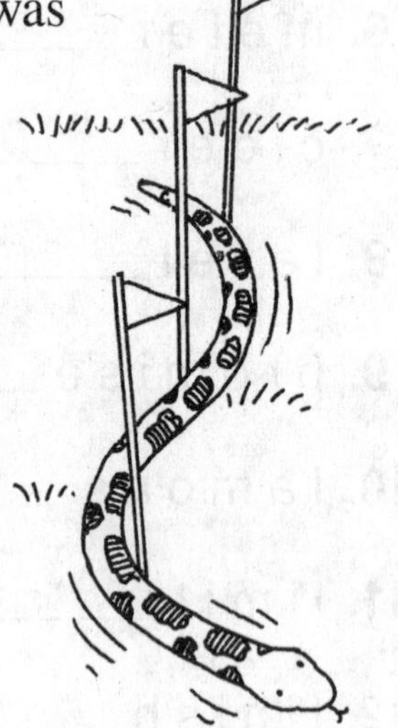

She made a straight line of poles in the ground. "Now, go in and out from each pole to the next."

Small Snake found that he was curving and slithering. "I know how to do it now!" he cried.

Raven said, "Caterpillar, you will watch out for Small Snake and be his ________________ until he grows up."

Name ________________________________

When authors write, they have a **purpose**, or reason, for what they want their work to do. They write fiction to **entertain**. They write nonfiction to **inform** or **explain**. They write essays to **persuade**.

Read the story excerpt below and decide on the author's purpose.

Once upon a time, Sammy Squirrel had a long, pointed tail, which did nothing to help him balance high up in the trees. Sammy had to move slowly and was always afraid of falling. Also, he had to remember to hold up his tail or the scales that covered it would scrape against the tree bark and let predators know where he was.

Agnes Armadillo, on the other hand, had a very bushy tail, but it was difficult to tuck all that lovely fur in when she had to roll up in a protective little ball.

1. What was the author's purpose in writing this story? ____________________

2. How did you decide on the author's purpose? ____________________

____

3. If the author wanted to inform readers, what would the author write?

____

____

4. If the author wanted to persuade readers, what would the author write?

____

____

Name ______________________________

As you read *Roadrunner's Dance*, fill in the Author's Purpose Map.

Clue	Clue	Clue

↓ ↓ ↓

Author's Purpose

How does the information you wrote in the Author's Purpose Map help you to evaluate *Roadrunner's Dance*?

Name ______________________________

As I read, I will pay attention to intonation and pacing.

	The monkey was having a simply splendid day. Then
9	she spotted a tiger bounding toward her through the jungle.
19	The monkey was sure the tiger would eat her on the spot.
31	She had to think fast.
36	The monkey covered a big pile of coconuts with some
46	banana leaves. She marched back and forth in front of it.
57	The tiger was intrigued by the monkey's odd behavior
66	and didn't attack. "What are you doing?" the tiger
75	demanded.
76	"I'm the king's guardian," **proclaimed** the monkey.
83	"I am guarding the king's food."
89	"Hmm," the tiger thought. "The king's food is bound to
99	be more delicious than that skinny monkey. Perhaps I can
109	trick the monkey into giving it to me."
117	"You are too small to be the king's **guardian**," said the
128	tiger. "A big animal like me should be the protector of
139	his food." 141

Comprehension Check

1. What is the author's purpose in this passage? **Author's Purpose**

2. What problem does the monkey face? How does she try to solve it? **Problem and Solution**

	Words Read	–	Number of Errors	=	Words Correct Score
First Read		–		=	
Second Read		–		=	

CA **R 1.1** Read narrative and expository text aloud with grade-appropriate fluency and accuracy and with appropriate **pacing**, **intonation**, and expression.

Name ______________________________

Foreshadowing hints at what is going to happen in a story without giving the story away. Authors use foreshadowing to build suspense. Dark clouds often foreshadow a storm.

Symbols are actions, objects, pictures, or sounds that people use to stand for important ideas and things. A dove is often a symbol for peace.

A. Read the passage. Then answer the questions.

Mouse and Bird were strolling through the desert. As always, Mouse was paying close attention to his surroundings. Bird was busy whistling. "We're walking past Tarantula's house," Mouse said. "Keep your eyes open!" Bird just kept whistling instead of paying attention. Mouse was safely past the rock when he looked behind him. He saw eight hairy legs stealthily creeping toward Bird.

1. What does Mouse's warning foreshadow? ______________________________

____

____

2. What detail about Bird's actions foreshadows that he might be in danger?

____

____

B. Read the question. Write your answers on the lines.

3. Which season is usually a symbol of new beginnings? Why? ______________

____

____

CA **R 2.3** Make and confirm predictions about text by using prior knowledge and ideas presented in the text itself, including illustrations, titles, topic sentences, important words, and foreshadowing clues.

Name ______________________________

A **synonym** is a word that means the same or almost the same as another word. For example, a synonym for *guardian* is *protector*.

A. Replace each of the words in parentheses with one of the following synonyms.

clumsy	nimble	announced	meddle	certain

1. "Don't (interfere) ______________ with my plans to be king of the road!"
2. The roadrunner was (awkward) ______________ when he first tried to run and jump.
3. He was (convinced) ______________ he could not learn.
4. Later, when Roadrunner danced in circles, you could see how (agile) ______________ he had become.
5. "Roadrunner is our hero!" the animals (proclaimed) ______________.

B. Write a sentence using a synonym for each of the words in dark type.

6. **frightened** and **trembled** ______________________________

____

7. **yelled** and **bragged** ______________________________

____

8. **hopped** and **quick** ______________________________

____

CA **R 1.2** Apply knowledge of word origins, derivations, **synonyms**, antonyms, and idioms to determine the meaning of words and phrases.

Name ____________________

Using the Word Study Steps

1. LOOK at the word.
2. SAY the word aloud.
3. STUDY the letters in the word.
4. WRITE the word.
5. CHECK the word.
   Did you spell the word right?
   If not, go back to step 1.

Rhyme Time

Circle the word in each row that rhymes with the spelling word on the left.

1. pity	party	city	penny
2. diver	driver	dove	diary
3. spoken	bitten	bike	broken
4. habit	rabbit	rated	rapid
5. river	shave	shiver	shatter
6. never	clever	clover	cluster
7. wiper	pipe	paper	piper
8. easel	dull	double	diesel
9. cider	reader	road	rider
10. stolen	swallow	swollen	swimming

CA LC 1.7 Spell correctly roots, inflections, suffixes and prefixes, and syllable constructions.

Name ____________________________________

A. There are six spelling mistakes in this letter. Circle the misspelled words. Write the words correctly on the lines below.

Dear Ms. Fisher,

I am writing because I think you are the best actress in the world! You have so much tallant. I want to be an actress, too. I am in the school play. I hope that someday I can be as fameus as you are.

My mom and I just saw your new movie. It was terrific. I especially loved the scene when you jumped into the rivvere. I could not believe that you were able to catch the man who was riding away in the stollan boat. I have nevar seen anything like it.

I have to go finnish my homework now. Thanks for making great movies! If you want to come see my play, it's this Saturday.

Regards,

Tamika Green

1. ____________ **3.** ____________ **5.** ____________

2. ____________ **4.** ____________ **6.** ____________

B. Writing Activity

Imagine that you are writing a play about something being stolen. Write a short scene for two of the characters. Use at least four spelling words in your scene.

____

____

____

____

____

____

CA LC 1.7 Spell correctly roots, inflections, suffixes and prefixes, and syllable constructions.

Name ________________________________

- Use ***the*** with singular nouns that name a particular person, place, or thing.
- Use ***the*** before all plural nouns.
- Use ***a*** and ***an*** with singular nouns.
- Use ***a*** if the next word starts with a consonant sound.
- Use ***an*** if the next word starts with a vowel sound.

Read each sentence. Put one line under each article. Put two lines under the noun that each article points out.

1. The snake bared his fangs.
2. Father and his family took a different path home.
3. Many villagers went to speak to the elders.
4. They went to see Desert Woman to ask a favor.
5. She placed a noisy rattle on Snake's tail.
6. Rattlesnake continued to threaten the animals.
7. They needed an animal that would make Rattlesnake behave.
8. Desert Woman molded a strange new bird from clay.
9. Roadrunner practiced dancing until he could twirl like a twister.
10. Roadrunner raced down the road to find Rattlesnake.
11. Rattlesnake let out an angry hiss.
12. He struck, but Roadrunner hopped out of the way.
13. Roadrunner danced around Rattlesnake like a whirlwind.
14. Rattlesnake made a promise not to frighten everyone any more.
15. All the children thanked Roadrunner for helping them.
16. Now the road was safe for everyone to use.

Name ____________________________

- Use ***a*** and ***an*** with singular nouns.
- Use ***a*** if the next word starts with a consonant sound.
- Use ***an*** if the next word starts with a vowel sound.
- Use ***the*** with singular nouns that name a particular person, place, or thing.
- Use ***the*** before all plural nouns.

Rewrite each sentence in the poster below. Remember to use *a*, *an*, and *the* correctly. Add articles where they are missing.

VICEROY ELEMENTARY SCHOOL ANNOUNCES
A THIRD ANNUAL ARTS AND CRAFTS SHOW!

show will take place on Saturday, March 28.
If you have a art project or an craft project to display,
please let fourth-grade art teacher know.
Gift card worth $30 will be awarded
to artist who wins first place.

Name ______________________________

Drill 3: Identifying Different Types of Leads

1. Review:

There are many ways to start a journal entry:

Four Types of Leads
Action
Dialogue
Observation
Question

2. Read:

"No dogs allowed," the manager told Kristy. ________________
Type of Lead

How was I going to finish all the cleaning before Mom got home? ____________
Type of Lead

The car stopped inches from Fluffy. ________________
Type of Lead

I saw the sun shine brightly on the dew-covered grass. ________________
Type of Lead

3. Write the correct type of lead next to each sentence above.

Name ______________________________

Sometimes two letters together stand for one vowel sound. This is called a **vowel team**. The vowel sound is usually long. When two vowels team up in a word, they stay in the same syllable.
oat/m**ea**l   r**ai**l/r**oa**d

Underline the vowel team in each word. Then write another word that has the same vowel team.

1. mailbox ____________
2. seashore ____________
3. soapdish ____________
4. steely ____________
5. boastful ____________
6. dreamlike ____________
7. staircase ____________
8. toaster ____________
9. unclear ____________
10. peering ____________

Name ______________________________

Practice

Vocabulary

A. Read the vocabulary words. Use the clues to complete the puzzle.

roamed completed journey natural relocated

Across

3. finished
4. trip
5. moved

Down

1. wandered
2. not artificial

B. Write a sentence using two of the words.

6. ______________________________

____

CA R 1.0 Word Analysis, Fluency, and Systematic Vocabulary Development

Name ______________________________

The **main idea** of a selection tells you what it is about. The supporting **details** in the selection help you understand the main idea.

Read the paragraph below. Then identify the main idea and three details that support it.

Cumberland Gap National Park is under attack! A plant called kudzu threatens the park's ecosystem. Few animals eat kudzu, and it grows so fast it's been called "the vine that ate the South." It can grow a foot a night! It grows even after it has been dosed with herbicide, or plant killer. That's bad news for native plants and trees. Kudzu grows right over them. It takes the sunlight plants need to live. Bits of kudzu came to Cumberland stuck to truck tires. The trucks were there to build a road. Now park rangers cut kudzu back. They apply herbicide to the plant's huge root. They could bring in goats because goats eat kudzu. But goats also eat native plants. Solving the kudzu problem will be tricky.

1. Main idea:

____

____

2. Supporting detail:

____

3. Supporting detail:

____

4. Supporting detail:

____

Name ______________________

As you read *Animals Come Home to Our National Parks*, fill in the Main Idea Chart.

Main Idea ______________________

____

____

Detail 1 ______________________

____

Detail 2 ______________________

____

Summary ______________________

____

____

____

How does the information you wrote in the Main Idea Chart help you to summarize *Animals Come Home to Our National Parks*?

Name ____________________

As I read, I will pay attention to the pronunciation of vocabulary words and other hard words.

	Acadia National Park has dark green mountains. When
8	you look down from these mountains you see the icy
18	Atlantic Ocean. You see ocean waves crashing against
26	rocky shores. These 48,000 acres (194 sq km) of **natural**
34	beauty have a long history. It is a history full of stories
46	about people who loved this land of mountain and sea.
56	These people worked to make sure that everyone could
65	enjoy it.
67	Acadia National Park is spread out over a group of
77	islands off the coast of Maine. Most of the park is on
89	Mount Desert Island. The park has beautiful freshwater
97	lakes and ponds. There are trails for hiking in the
107	mountains or walking by the shore.
113	As you read, you will learn about the history of
123	this park. 125

Comprehension Check

1. What is the main idea of the first paragraph? **Main Idea and Details**

2. What details would you use to describe the natural beauty of the park? **Main Idea and Details**

	Words Read	–	Number of Errors	=	Words Correct Score
First Read		–		=	
Second Read		–		=	

CA **R 1.1** Read narrative and expository text aloud with grade-appropriate fluency and accuracy and with appropriate pacing, intonation, and expression.

Practice

Study Skill: Dictionary

Name ________________________________

A **dictionary** entry lists more than just a word's meanings. It also includes its pronunciation, part of speech, and examples of how to use the word.

Read the dictionary entry below. Then answer the questions that follow.

lively 1. full of energy. The *lively* puppies romped around the room.
2. bright. The walls of Emma's room were painted a *lively* pink.
live·ly līv´ lē *adjective,* **livelier, liveliest.**

1. What is the entry word? ________________
2. How many syllables does this word have? ________________
3. To pronounce the word *lively*, is the vowel in the first syllable long or short? ________________
4. What part of speech is *lively*? ________________
5. Which definition best describes a fourth-grade class at recess?

____

6. What other forms of *lively* are listed in the entry? ________________

____

CA **W 1.7** Use various reference materials (e.g., **dictionary**, thesaurus, card catalog, encyclopedia, online information) as an aid to writing.

Name ____

Description Writing Frame

A. Summarize *Animals Come Home to Our National Parks.* Use the Description Writing Frame below.

People are trying to restore the damaged __________ in our National Parks.

First, they are ____
____
____
____.

This is important **because** ____________________________________
____
____
____.

They are also ____
____
____
____.

This is important **because** ____________________________________
____
____
____.

B. Rewrite the completed summary on another sheet of paper. Keep it as a model for writing a summary of an article or selection using this text structure.

Name ______________________________

Many English words are formed by adding word parts, such as prefixes and suffixes, to a basic word, or root word. Many words have roots that come from Latin, the language of ancient Rome.

- Words that have the root *locat* have to do with places.
- Words that have the root *duc* have to do with leading.

Complete each sentence with a word from the box that takes the place of the underlined words.

educate	relocate	location	conduct	deduce

1. When people build in places where animals live, animals are sometimes forced to move to a new place of activity or residence. ______________
2. Many zoos and parks lead or guide tours to help people learn about the animals that live there. ______________
3. Many experts can be led to a conclusion about what kinds of animals live in an area just by looking at animal tracks. ______________
4. Some parks and zoos move to a different place animals whose habitats have been destroyed. ______________
5. It is a good idea to lead yourself to learn about the animals that live in your community. ______________

CA **R 1.4** Know common roots and affixes derived from Greek and Latin and use this knowledge to analyze the meaning of complex words (e.g., *international*).

Practice

Spelling: Vowel Teams

Name ______________________________

Using the Word Study Steps

1. LOOK at the word.
2. SAY the word aloud.
3. STUDY the letters in the word.
4. WRITE the word.
5. CHECK the word.
   Did you spell the word right?
   If not, go back to step 1.

Complete each word with a vowel team from the box below to write a spelling word. Then write the word.

ai	ee	ua	ou	ea	oa	oo	ei

1. rep___ ___t ______________
2. disc___ ___nt ______________
3. ___ ___rfare ______________
4. betw___ ___n ______________
5. appr___ ___ch ______________
6. dom___ ___n ______________
7. ben___ ___th ______________
8. merm___ ___d ______________
9. pers___ ___de ______________
10. comp___ ___nd ______________
11. ___ ___ght___ ___n ______________
12. bab___ ___n ______________
13. sl___ ___pless ______________
14. tr___ ___ner ______________
15. def___ ___t ______________

CA **LC 1.7** Spell correctly roots, inflections, suffixes and prefixes, and syllable constructions.

Name ______________________

Practice

Spelling: Vowel Teams

A. There are six spelling mistakes in this passage. Circle the misspelled words. Write the words correctly on the lines below.

On Saturday, the eightene members of my nature club are going camping at a state park. To prepare us, our leader gave us a set of rules. He said:

1. No radios. It will defeet the purpose of the trip if you can't enjoy the sounds of nature.
2. You are in the animals' domane. Leave it just like you found it.
3. Listen carefully. I want everyone to be safe, and I don't want to repeet myself.
4. Have fun!

I'm sure it will be a sleapless night, but I know it will increese my love of nature.

1. ______________ 3. ______________ 5. ______________

2. ______________ 4. ______________ 6. ______________

B. Write about a trip you have taken to a park or other natural area. Use at least four spelling words in your paragraph.

____

____

____

____

____

____

____

CA **LC 1.7** Spell correctly roots, inflections, suffixes and prefixes, and syllable constructions.

Name ______________________________

- Add *-er* to most adjectives to compare two people, places, or things.
- Add *-est* to most adjectives to compare more than two.
- For adjectives ending in *e*, drop the *e* before adding *-er* or *-est.*
- For adjectives ending in a consonant and *y*, change the *y* to *i* before adding *-er* or *-est.*
- For adjectives that have a single vowel before a final consonant, double the final consonant before adding *-er* or *-est.*

Rewrite the sentences below, correcting the form or spelling of the underlined adjective.

1. After the sun went down, the air felt chilliest than before.

____

2. I think fish feel freeer in the ocean than they do in tanks.

____

3. Dad caught the bigest fish of all.

____

4. I wonder which ocean is the saltyest.

____

5. The dolphin is one of the smartiest animals.

____

6. The water is calmmer than it was yesterday.

____

7. My clothes are wettest than they were this morning.

____

8. That shark has the paleest skin I've ever seen.

____

Rewrite the title and each sentence in the response to literature below. Remember to use *-er* and *-est* endings correctly with adjectives. Be sure to capitalize proper nouns, names, and titles.

Response to "exploring the undersea Territory"

I enjoyed reading this article. After learning about undersea explorers, I think that the work they do is strangeer and scaryer than most people's jobs. But it is also more interesting.

One of the braveest explorers of all is sylvia Earle. She was nicknamed "Her deepness" because in 1979 she made the deeper ocean dive any human being had ever made alone. She went on to work as a businesswoman and as a scientist at the National oceanic and Atmospheric Administration.

____

____

____

____

____

____

____

____

____

____

____

____

____

Name ______________________________

Writing Rubric			
4 Excellent	3 Good	2 Fair	1 Unsatisfactory
Ideas and Content/ Genre	Ideas and Content/ Genre	Ideas and Content/ Genre	Ideas and Content/ Genre
Organization and Focus	Organization and Focus	Organization and Focus	Organization and Focus
Sentence Structure/ Fluency	Sentence Structure/ Fluency	Sentence Structure/ Fluency	Sentence Structure/ Fluency
Conventions	Conventions	Conventions	Conventions
Word Choice	Word Choice	Word Choice	Word Choice
Voice	Voice	Voice	Voice
Presentation	Presentation	Presentation	Presentation

Name ____

Practice

Phonics: *r*-Controlled Vowel Syllables

The schwa + ***r*** or **/ər/** sound is what you hear at the end of ***collar*, *danger*,** and ***victor***. Notice that this sound can be spelled in three different ways—***ar***, ***er***, and ***or***.

barber	zipper	anchor	harbor	popular	collar

A. Use the words in the box to complete each sentence. Underline the letters that make the /ər/ sound in each word.

1. Every time my clever ________________ cuts my hair, he creates a work of art.
2. The Flemish oil paintings in the north tower are the most ________________ exhibit in the museum.
3. My favorite collage is the one I made with the ________________ from an old pair of trousers.
4. Aunt Susie finished her watercolor painting of the clipper ships in the ________________.
5. I put a ________________ and leash on my dog when we go for a walk in the park.
6. Uncle Tim thinks the old rusty tanker ________________ in his front yard is beautiful!

B. Now look for other examples of the /ər/ sound in the sentences and underline them as well.

CA **R 1.0** Word Analysis, Fluency, and Systematic Vocabulary Development

Name ______________________________

suburbs	brittle	current
reef	eventually	partnership

A. Complete each sentence with a word from the box.

1. The blizzard closed the airport for several hours, but planes ________________ were able to take off.

2. My father took the train from our station in the ________________ into the city each morning.

3. During the storm the wind snapped the ________________ tree branch.

4. The hidden ________________ ripped into the bottom of the boat.

5. The fast-moving ________________ of the river swept the dead tree out to sea.

6. My friends and I set up a business ________________.

B. Choose four of the vocabulary words and use them in three sentences.

7. ____

____

8. ____

____

9. ____

____

Name ______________________________

When you **compare** two things, you look at ways in which they are alike. When you **contrast** them, you focus on how they are different.

A. Read the passage about sharks and dolphins below. Then follow the instructions that follow.

Dolphins and sharks both live in the ocean, but they are different in many ways. Dolphins are not fish, but warm-blooded mammals. Dolphins have lungs and come up to the surface to breathe.

Sharks are fish, with gills instead of lungs. Some sharks live deep in the ocean, while others live near the surface.

Sharks and dolphins are alike in some ways, too. Both eat fish, and some kinds live together in rivers and lakes in Central and South America.

B. Compare sharks and dolphins and list two ways that they are alike.

1. ______________________________

____

2. ______________________________

____

Contrast sharks and dolphins and list two ways in which they are different.

3. ______________________________

____

4. ______________________________

____

CA **R 2.1** Identify structural patterns found in informational text (e.g., compare and contrast, cause and effect, sequential or chronological order, proposition and support) to strengthen comprehension.

Name ____

As you read *At Home in the Coral Reef*, fill in the Venn Diagrams.

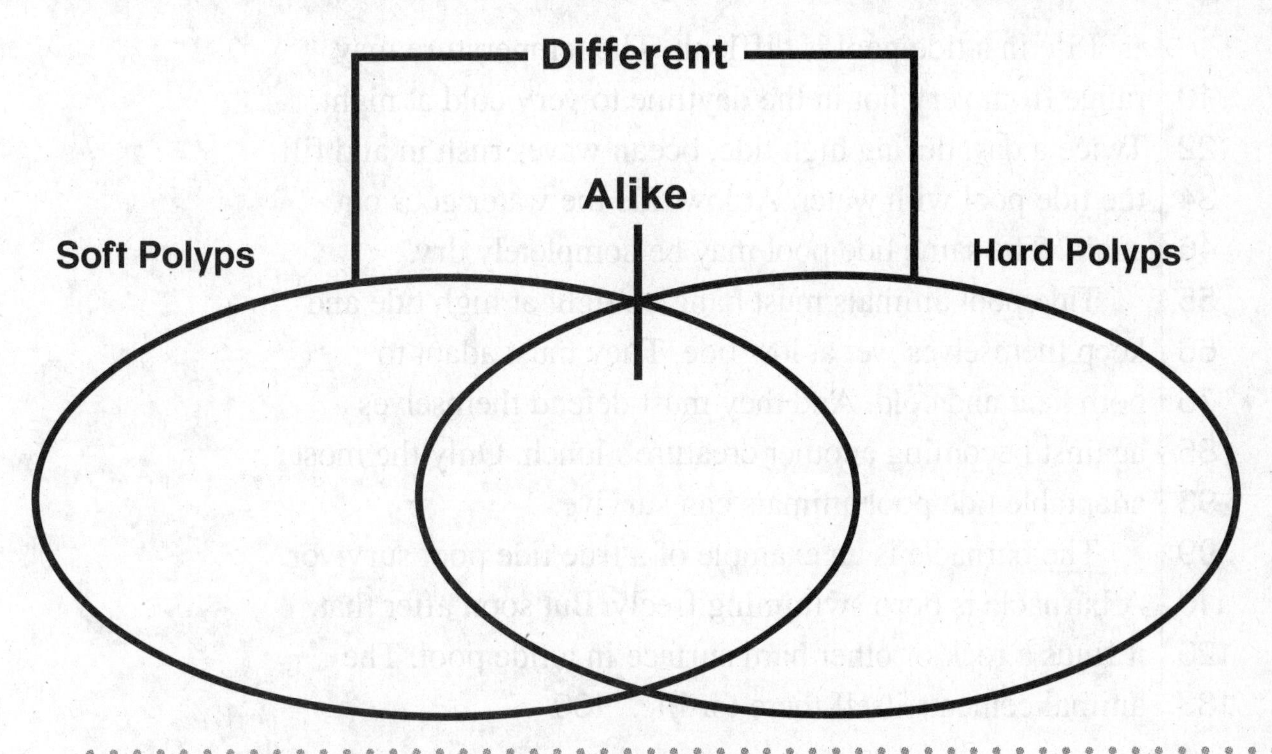

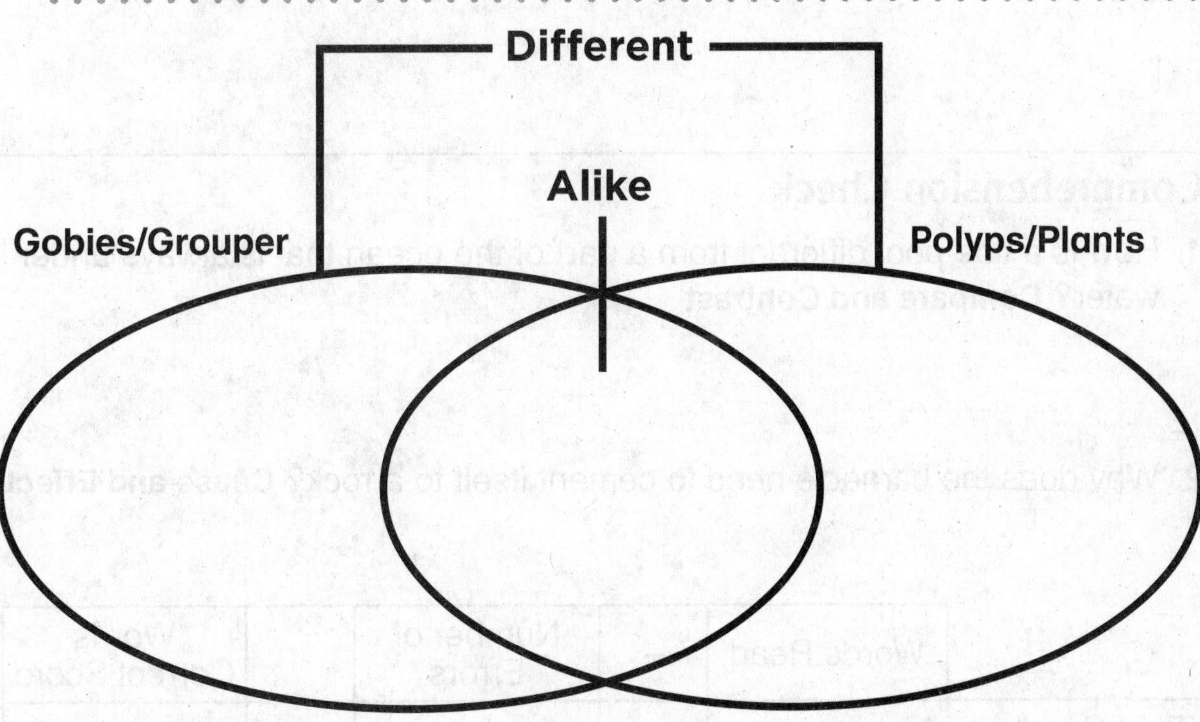

How does completing the Venn Diagrams help you to analyze the text structure of *At Home in the Coral Reef*?

R 2.1 Identify structural patterns found in informational text (e.g., compare and contrast, cause and effect, sequential or chronological order, proposition and support) to strengthen comprehension.

Name ______________________________

Practice

Fluency: Intonation and Expression

As I read, I will pay attention to my intonation and expression.

	Life in a tide pool is difficult. The temperature may
10	range from very hot in the daytime to very cold at night.
22	Twice a day, during high tide, ocean waves rush in and fill
34	the tide pool with water. At low tide the water goes out
46	again. The same tide pool may be completely dry.
55	Tide pool animals must hang on tight at high tide and
66	keep themselves wet at low tide. They must adapt to
76	both heat and cold. And they must defend themselves
85	against becoming another creature's lunch. Only the most
93	adaptable tide pool animals can survive.
99	The barnacle is an example of a true tide pool survivor.
110	A barnacle is born swimming freely. But soon after that,
120	it finds a rock or other hard surface in a tide pool. The
133	animal cements itself there for life. 139

Comprehension Check

1. How is a tide pool different from a part of the ocean that is always under water? **Compare and Contrast**

2. Why does the barnacle need to cement itself to a rock? **Cause and Effect**

	Words Read	–	Number of Errors	=	Words Correct Score
First Read		–		=	
Second Read		–		=	

R 1.1 Read narrative and expository text aloud with grade-appropriate fluency and accuracy and with appropriate pacing, intonation, and expression.

Name ______________________________

A **protagonist** is the main character in a story. In a myth, the protagonist is usually a god or goddess, or a heroic character. **Hyperbole** uses describing words to exaggerate. It is a kind of figurative language that calls attention to how someone or something looks, acts, or feels. Examples of hyperbole are *a million grains of sand*, and *a mile-long tail*. Writers use hyperbole for emphasis, to create a picture in the reader's mind, or to add humor or suspense.

A. Read each sentence. If it contains hyperbole, underline the phrase that is hyperbole. If it doesn't, put an X in the box.

1. The trip to the reef lasted forever. ☐

2. The reef itself must have been a million miles long. ☐

3. The fish swam in and out of the many holes in the coral. ☐

4. Underwater, the sea plants were a soft green. ☐

5. The fish in the reef swam faster than lightning. ☐

6. A coral reef has many unique plants and animals. ☐

7. I would give my right arm to go back to the reef. ☐

8. Scientific research on the many forms of underwater plant and animal life is extremely important. ☐

B. Circle the letter of the correct answer.

9. What is a protagonist?

a. a story's main event **b.** a story's setting **c.** a story's main character

10. In what kind of story is the protagonist usually a god or goddess?

a. a humorous story **b.** a myth **c.** a mystery

Name ______________________

Context clues can help readers determine the meaning of an unfamiliar word. Sometimes writers will provide context clues through a **description** that makes the meaning of a word clearer.
Example: *My uncle could never eat clams or oysters because he was allergic to* ***mollusks***.
You can use the context clues *clams* and *oysters* to figure out the meaning of the word ***mollusks***.

Underline the context clues that describe the word in dark type. Then write the word's definition.

1. I saw all kinds of **marine** life swimming underwater in the ocean.

   Definition: ______________________

2. After the earthquake, there were a few smaller **tremors** that shook the ground.

   Definition: ______________________

3. Some fish feed on **plankton** because these tiny plants and animals are very nutritious.

   Definition: ______________________

4. To put out the fire, the man **doused** the flames with a bucket of water.

   Definition: ______________________

5. The captain pulled the **rudder** hard to the left to steer the ship away from the rocks.

   Definition: ______________________

6. The **brilliant** sunshine streamed in through the window and lit up the room.

   Definition: ______________________

Name ______________________________

Using the Word Study Steps

1. LOOK at the word.
2. SAY the word aloud.
3. STUDY the letters in the word.
4. WRITE the word.
5. CHECK the word.
   Did you spell the word right?
   If not, go back to step 1.

Find and Circle

The spelling words are hiding in this puzzle. See if you can find and circle all 20 words.

rwxcheddarttwypowdermbhgypopulartwrqepepper
qanchortwgraderxcwrqtttrdaughteroophhrharbort
zipperodorwtqqfgllpyttdangerrwdgrocerptkknlwqo
trwybarberjhtenterhtankerplkjmnhhnjmkptpolar
fwcollarywqelevatorssingerttwklppmnowvictorpt

CA **LC 1.7** Spell correctly roots, inflections, suffixes and prefixes, and syllable constructions.

Name ____________________

A. Proofreading

There are six spelling mistakes in this report. Circle the misspelled words. Write the words correctly on the lines below.

A Studio Visit

As I approached the building, I was excited. A very populer painter, Anne Smith, had agreed to show me around her studio. I had never been to an artist's studio before.

A sign above the door said, "Entar here." I walked in and took the ellevater to the second floor.

As soon as the door opened, I could smell a weird odar. Anne met me in the hall and explained that the smell was from her oil paints. When we walked into her studio, I forgot about the smell. There were paintings everywhere! My favorite was a picture of Anne's daughtor standing in front of a huge ship in the harber.

Anne is a great painter. I am so glad that she let me visit her studio.

1. ____________ **3.** ____________ **5.** ____________

2. ____________ **4.** ____________ **6.** ____________

B. Writing Activity

Imagine that you are an artist. Describe your latest work of art. Be creative! Use at least four spelling words in your description.

____

____

____

____

____

CA **LC 1.7** Spell correctly roots, inflections, suffixes and prefixes, and syllable constructions.

Name ______________________________

- For long adjectives, use *more* and *most* to compare people, places, or things.
- Use *more* to compare two people, places, or things.
- Use *most* to compare more than two.
- When you use *more* or *most*, do not use the ending *-er* or *-est*.

Rewrite each sentence. Use the correct form of the adjective.

1. Harlem is the more excitingest place I've ever been.

____

2. The sounds of the traffic outside made me feel more awaker than at home.

____

____

3. At first, Aunt Nanette seemed more caringer than Uncle Romie.

____

4. My visit to my grandparents' house is the most peacefulest time I can remember.

____

____

5. My aunt and uncle are most importanter to me than they used to be.

____

____

6. Uncle Romie is the most artisticest person I know.

____

7. I was more carefuller with this collage than I usually am.

____

8. My mother makes the more excellentest pepper jelly I have ever tasted.

____

____

Name ______________________________

Practice

Grammar: Comparing with *More* and *Most*

- For long adjectives, use *more* and *most* to compare people, places, or things.
- Use *more* to compare two people, places, or things.
- Use *most* to compare more than two.

Rewrite each sentence in the introduction speech below. Remember to use *more* and *most* correctly with adjectives. Use a comma after an introductory word used at the beginning of a sentence. Use a comma when the first word in the sentence addresses someone by name.

Class I would like to introduce my Uncle Romie to you. I met him last summer when I visited New York. He is the most creativest, most imaginativest person I know! His work is more unusualer and more powerfuler than any painting in a museum. Is he a painter? Is he a photographer? Is he a writer? No he's all of those at once. He puts paint, pictures, newspapers, magazines, and other things together to make the most amazing collages. His collage of Harlem is the more joyfulest picture I've ever seen. Yes I have also started making collages, just like Uncle Romie.

____

____

____

____

____

____

____

____

____

____

CA LC 1.0 Written and Oral English Language Conventions

Name ______________________________

Drill 1: Adding a Moment to a Student's Journal

1. **Read:**
   1. The dog started barking as I walked by the house.
   2. I bit into the sandwich and felt something strange.
   3. She spilled her lunch tray on the floor.
   4. They ran to the door.
   5. I opened my eyes and looked at the ceiling.

2. **Write** ONE sentence that shows what happens NEXT in each moment.
   1. The dog started barking as I walked by the house.
   2. I bit into the sandwich and felt something strange.
   3. She spilled her lunch tray on the floor.
   4. They ran to the door.
   5. I opened my eyes and looked at the ceiling.

Extra Practice: Choose one moment and write a few more sentences about what happened.

____

____

____

Name ______________________________

Practice

Phonics: Consonant + *le* Syllables

The **/əl/** sound is what you hear at the end of ***double***, ***medal***, ***vessel***, and ***fossil***. Notice the four different letter pairs that can stand for the sound.

local	little	adaptable	channel	pupil
kettle	verbal	uncle	natural	

Choose a word from the box to fill in each blank. Underline the letters that make the /əl/ sound in each word.

1. A ________________ community group is working to protect the ________________ habitat of wild horses.

2. ________________ Cal, my grandfather's brother, used to work on a farm that caught and tamed wild horses.

3. For homework, the ________________ watched a documentary about wild horses on the nature ________________.

4. Wild horses are not the most ________________ animals, which makes them difficult to tame.

5. When working with horses, the trainer would call out ________________ commands.

6. I poured a ________________ more water from the ________________ into my tea cup.

CA R 1.0 Word Analysis, Fluency, and Systematic Vocabulary Development

Name ______________________________

dove	unique	tangles
encounter	massive	rumbling

A. Fill in each blank with the correct vocabulary word from the list at the top of the page.

1. The ______________ boulder weighed over ten tons.
2. After a day at the ocean, the girl's long hair became a mess of ______________.
3. To make sure that her quilt would be ______________, Grandma used an unusual pattern for organizing her patches.
4. The hawk ______________ quickly to catch the rabbit.
5. My grandfather did not expect to ______________ a bear on the path.
6. The ______________ of the thunder scared my dog.

B. Choose three vocabulary words and use them in one sentence.

7. ____

Name ______________________________

Practice

Comprehension: Sequence

The chronological order of events in a story is the order in which things happen. Keeping track of the **sequence**, or order of events, helps you make sense of what is happening in a story.

Read the story below. Then number the events that follow to show the chronological order.

Miranda's parents were planning a trip to Mexico to go whale watching. Miranda's mother bought airline tickets on a travel Web site. Miranda's father asked his boss for time off. Miranda asked a neighbor to feed the family pets. Miranda's mother asked the post office to hold their mail.

On the day of the trip, the family drove to the airport. They stood in line and went through security. Finally they boarded the airplane and took off for Mexico.

1. Miranda's mother asked the post office to hold the mail. ______

2. They stood in line and went through security. ______

3. The family boarded the plane and took off for Mexico. ______

4. Miranda's parents were planning a trip to Mexico. ______

5. Miranda's father asked his boss for time off. ______

6. Miranda's mother bought airline tickets on a travel Web site. ______

7. Miranda asked a neighbor to feed the family pets. ______

8. On the day of the trip, the family drove to the airport. ______

R 2.1 Identify structural patterns found in informational text (e.g., compare and contrast, cause and effect, sequential or chronological order, proposition and support) to strengthen comprehension.

Name ___________________________________

As you read *Adelina's Whales*, fill in the Sequence Chart.

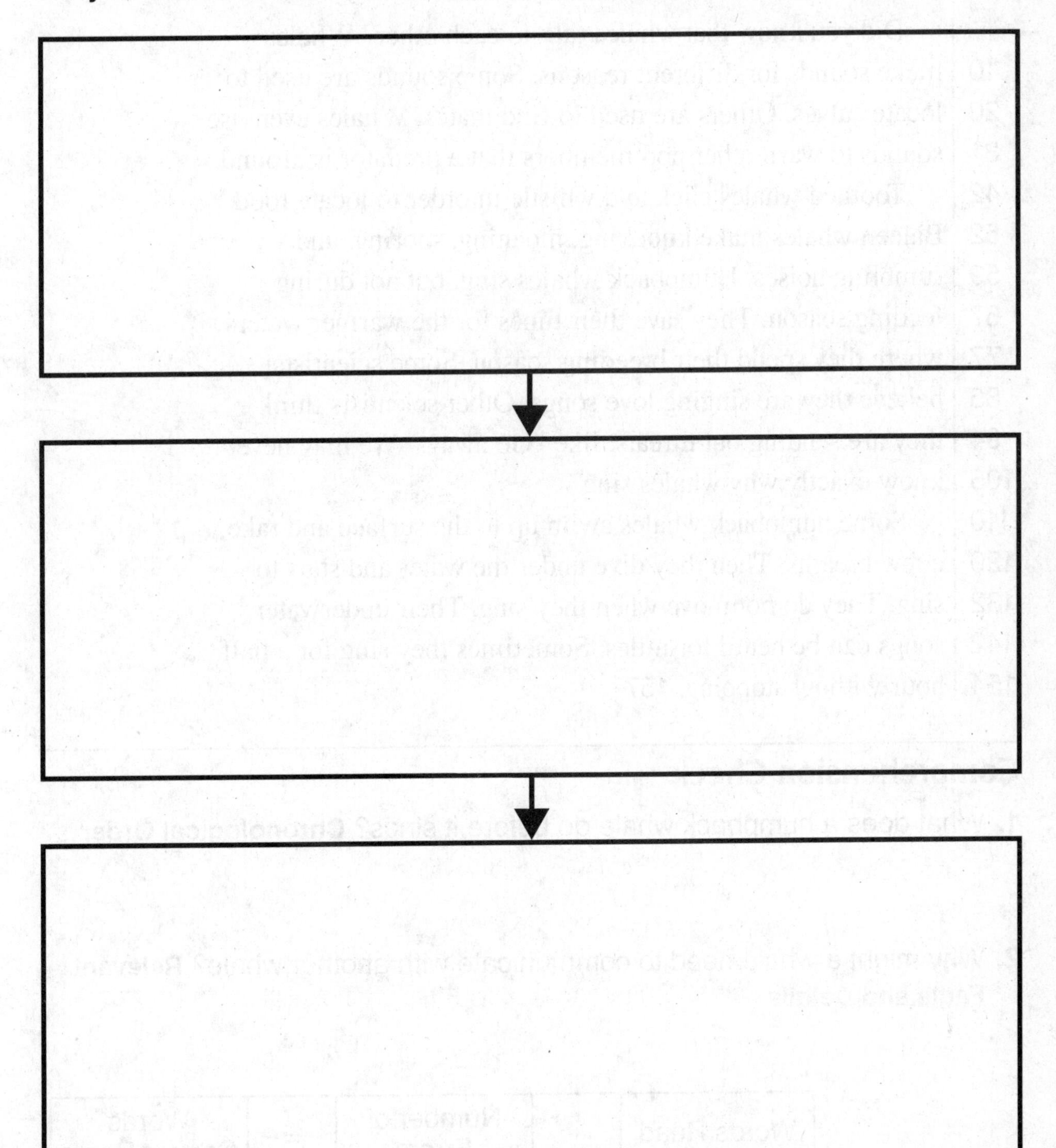

How does the information you wrote in the Sequence Chart help you to analyze the text structure of *Adelina's Whales*?

R 2.1 Identify structural patterns found in informational text (e.g., compare and contrast, cause and effect, sequential or chronological order, proposition and support) to strengthen comprehension.

Name ________________________________

Practice

Fluency: Pacing and Expression

As I read, I will pay attention to pacing and expression.

Did you know that whales talk to each other? Whales
10 make sounds for different reasons. Some sounds are used to
20 locate calves. Others are used to find mates. Whales even use
31 sounds to warn other pod members that a predator is around.
42 Toothed whales click and whistle in order to locate food.
52 Baleen whales make knocking, moaning, snoring, and
59 rumbling noises. Humpback whales sing, but not during
67 feeding season. They save their tunes for the warmer waters
77 where they spend their breeding season. Some scientists
85 believe they are singing love songs. Other scientists think
94 they are sending out threats, like "Go away!" We may never
105 know exactly why whales sing.
110 Some humpback whales swim up to the surface and take
120 a few breaths. Then they dive under the water and start to
132 sing. They do not move when they sing. Their underwater
142 songs can be heard for miles. Sometimes they sing for a half
154 hour without stopping. 157

Comprehension Check

1. What does a humpback whale do before it sings? **Chronological Order**

2. Why might a whale need to communicate with another whale? **Relevant Facts and Details**

	Words Read	–	Number of Errors	=	Words Correct Score
First Read		–		=	
Second Read		–		=	

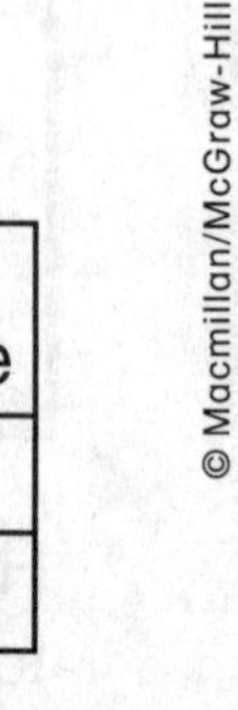

R 1.1 Read narrative and expository text aloud with grade-appropriate fluency and accuracy and with appropriate pacing, intonation, and expression.

Name ______________________________

The **rhyme scheme** of a poem is the pattern of rhymes at the end of each line. The poem's **meter** is the way that accented and unaccented syllables are arranged in the poem. You can think of it as the poem's rhythm.

1. **Read the following limerick by Edward Lear. Circle the rhyming words at the end of each line. Then put an *a* next to the first set of rhyming words and a *b* next to the second set of rhyming words to identify the poem's rhyme scheme.**

   There was an Old Man with a beard, _______

   Who said "It is just as I feared!— _______

   Two Owls and a Hen, _______

   Four Larks and a Wren, _______

   Have all built their nests in my beard!" _______

2. **Read the first line of the poem. How would you describe the meter of this line?**

   ____

3. **Now write your own limerick below.**

   ____

   ____

   ____

   ____

   ____

Name ______________________________

Practice

Vocabulary Strategy: Homographs

Homographs are words that have the same spelling but different meanings. They may also have different pronunciations.

A. Read the list of homographs and their meanings. Then read the sentences and decide the meaning of the underlined homograph. Write the letter of the correct meaning in the blank next to the sentence.

dove – a. past tense of dive **b.** a kind of bird

fluke – c. part of a whale's tail **d.** something lucky

1. The whale splashed the surface of the water with its fluke. ______

2. The eagle dove for its prey. ______

3. It was a fluke that my mother won the game. ______

4. The bird watchers saw a mourning dove sitting in a tree. ______

B. Pick another homograph. Write one sentence for each meaning of the word.

5. ____

____

6. ____

____

Name ______________________________

Using the Word Study Steps

1. LOOK at the word.
2. SAY the word aloud.
3. STUDY the letters in the word.
4. WRITE the word.
5. CHECK the word.
   Did you spell the word right?
   If not, go back to step 1.

Find and Circle

Find and circle the hidden spelling words.

```
S  B  U  B  B  L  E  X  S  V  P
P  E  B  B  L  E  X  Q  Y  X  E
E  P  A  D  D  L  E  V  M  Z  D
C  H  A  N  N  E  L  V  B  X  A
I  U  N  C  L  E  O  Q  O  S  L
A  V  K  Z  D  O  C  I  L  E  K
L  X  L  X  Z  B  A  V  K  T  K
P  V  E  S  S  E  L  Q  P  T  M
U  Z  V  Z  Q  N  B  U  G  L  E
P  E  N  C  I  L  X  Z  Z  E  D
I  Q  K  T  U  R  T  L  E  X  A
L  X  T  O  T  A  L  O  R  A  L
```


CA **LC 1.7** Spell correctly roots, inflections, suffixes and prefixes, and syllable constructions.

Name ______________________________

Practice

Spelling: Consonant + *le* Syllables

A. Proofreading

There are six spelling mistakes in this letter. Circle the misspelled words. Write the words correctly on the lines below.

Dear Dr. Carter,

I am a pupel in the fourth grade. Our class is studying wild horses. I saw you on the news last night on Channal 5 talking about how our country should deal with mustangs. Since you are a lokil expert, I wanted to see if you would come and speak to my class.

We have learned a lot about these animals. They are a symble of the American West because they are free and run fast in wide open spaces. There is a totel of 45,000 wild horses left in the United States. We are also learning about how some groups want to save these animals.

I hope you can come and visit my class. It would be very speciol to us.

Regards,

Ava Recio

1. ______________ 3 ______________ 5. ______________

2. ______________ 4. ______________ 6. ______________

B. Writing Activity

What is your favorite animal? Write a paragraph about it using at least four spelling words in your description.

____

____

____

____

____

____

CA LC 1.7 Spell correctly roots, inflections, suffixes and prefixes, and syllable constructions.

Name ______________________________

- Use *worse* to compare two people, places, or things.
- Use *worst* to compare more than two.

Write *worse* or *worst* to complete each sentence correctly.

1. The invention of barbed-wire fences made life ____________ for wild horses than before.
2. During the ____________ period, the population of horses fell below 17,000.
3. Hunger and thirst were the ____________ threats to horses.
4. Seeing wild horses in fenced feedlots made Dayton Hyde feel ____________ than he had for a long time.
5. The ranch was no ____________ than the feedlot.
6. The thought of the horses breaking down the fence was Dayton's ____________ fear.
7. Conditions were ____________ for horses after more land was settled.
8. The cold felt ____________ for the cowboys than it did for the horses.
9. This is the ____________ time to ride a horse.
10. My saddle sore is no ____________ than yours, I suppose.
11. That's not the ____________ riding I've ever seen.
12. That trail is much ____________ than this trail.

Name ______________________________

Rewrite each sentence in the scientific observation below. Remember to use forms of *good* and *bad* correctly.

QUESTION: What is the bestest way to approach a horse?
OBSERVATIONS: Calm horses have relaxed muscles, heads, and necks. Frightened horses may raise their heads and tense their muscles. Flattened ears are one of the most worst signs of fear.

Alan and Maria approached the horse named Bertha. The trainer, Marcos, was with them. (It is always goodest to have adults present for safety.) When Alan walked noisily toward Bertha from behind, her signs of fear grew worser. When Maria walked slowly and quietly toward Bertha from the left front side, Bertha stayed more calmer. She seemed to like this approach much more better.
CONCLUSION: Approaching a horse from the front or side is gooder than approaching from behind.

____

____

____

____

____

____

____

____

____

____

____

____

____

____

____

Name ______________________________

Drill 3: Brainstorming as Many Moments as Possible!

1. Think about what happens at a birthday party.

2. Brainstorm some moments that happen at a birthday party.

For example:

1. guests arrive
2. playing party games
3. ______________________________
4. ______________________________
5. ______________________________
6. ______________________________

3. Think about another kind of day that was special to you.

4. Write a title for your special day: ______________________________

5. Brainstorm some moments from that special day.

1. ______________________________
2. ______________________________
3. ______________________________
4. ______________________________
5. ______________________________
6. ______________________________
7. ______________________________

Extra Practice: Think of MORE moments to add to your brainstorm.

____

____

____

____

Name ______________________________

Listen for the final /**ən**/ sounds at the end of the following words:

wood**en**	oft**en**	rais**in**	reas**on**	bac**on**

The /**ən**/ sounds can be spelled ***-en***, ***-in***, or ***-on***.

bacon	proven	button	eleven	cousin	dozen
women	reason	shaken	listen	common	cotton

Write a word from the box to complete each sentence. Underline the letters that represent the /ən/ sounds.

1. Were there any ________________ at the mining camps?
2. Nine plus two is one less than a ________________.
3. Do you know the ________________ why the computer turned into a time machine?
4. Miners fried up lots of ________________ for their breakfasts.
5. General stores in San Francisco sold yards of ________________ for all the clothes the miners would need.
6. My great-grandfather had a ________________ who was a gold miner.
7. The earthquake left them feeling very ________________ up.
8. I love to ________________ to stories about the Gold Rush.
9. Most of the miners could sew a patch or a ________________ on their clothes.
10. The pigeon is a ________________ bird in many cities.

Name ______________________________

items clustered bidding glistened overflowing sturdy

Use the clues below to complete the vocabulary word puzzle.

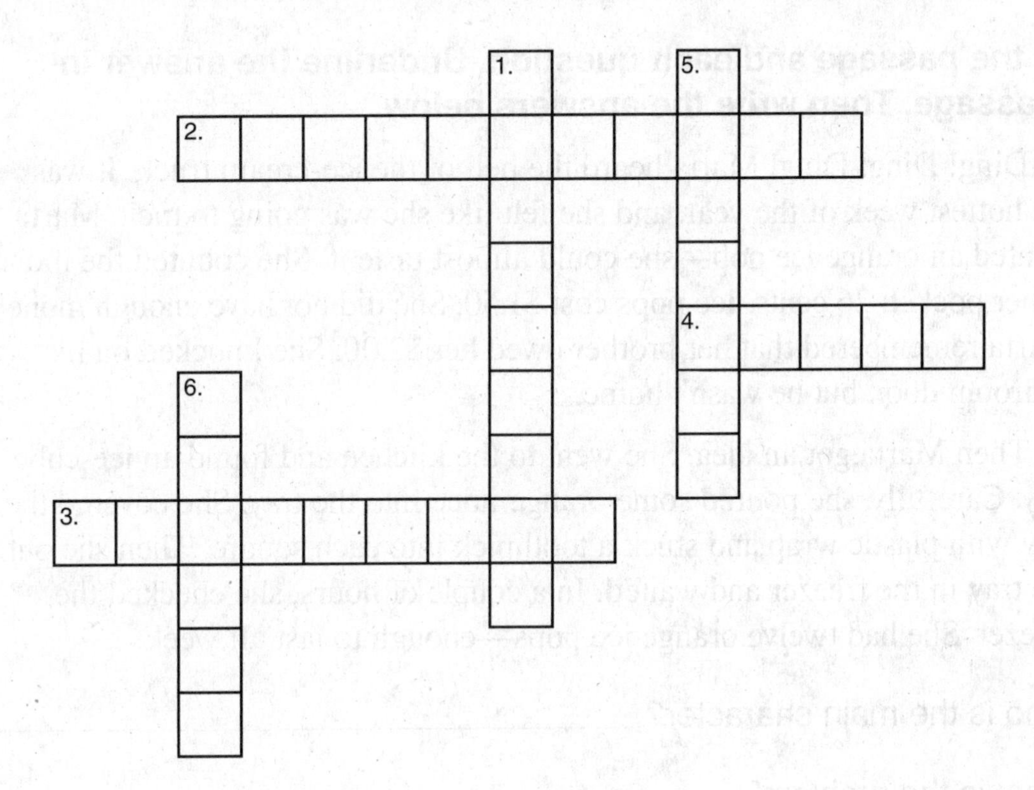

Across

2. spilling out of a full container
3. grouped together
4. two or more things in a group

Down

1. sparkled and shined
5. making an offer of money for something
6. strong and well built

Name ______________________________

When you read a narrative, look for the **problem** that the main character has. Notice the steps the character takes to find the **solution** to the problem.

Read the passage and each question. Underline the answer in the passage. Then write the answers below.

Ding! Ding! Ding! Marta heard the bell of the ice-cream truck. It was the hottest week of the year, and she felt like she was going to melt. Marta wanted an orange ice pop—she could almost taste it. She counted the money in her pocket: 26 cents. Ice pops cost $1.50. She did not have enough money. Marta remembered that her brother owed her $2.00. She knocked on his bedroom door, but he wasn't home.

Then Marta got an idea. She went to the kitchen and found an ice-cube tray. Carefully, she poured some orange juice into the tray. She covered the tray with plastic wrap and stuck a toothpick into each square. Then she put the tray in the freezer and waited. In a couple of hours, she checked the freezer. She had twelve orange ice pops—enough to last all week.

1. Who is the main character? ______________________________

2. What is the problem? ______________________________

____

3. What is the first thing Marta does to solve her problem? ______________

____

4. How does Marta solve her problem? ______________________________

____

5. What might happen next? ______________________________

Name ____________________

As you read *Leah's Pony*, fill in the Problem and Solution Chart.

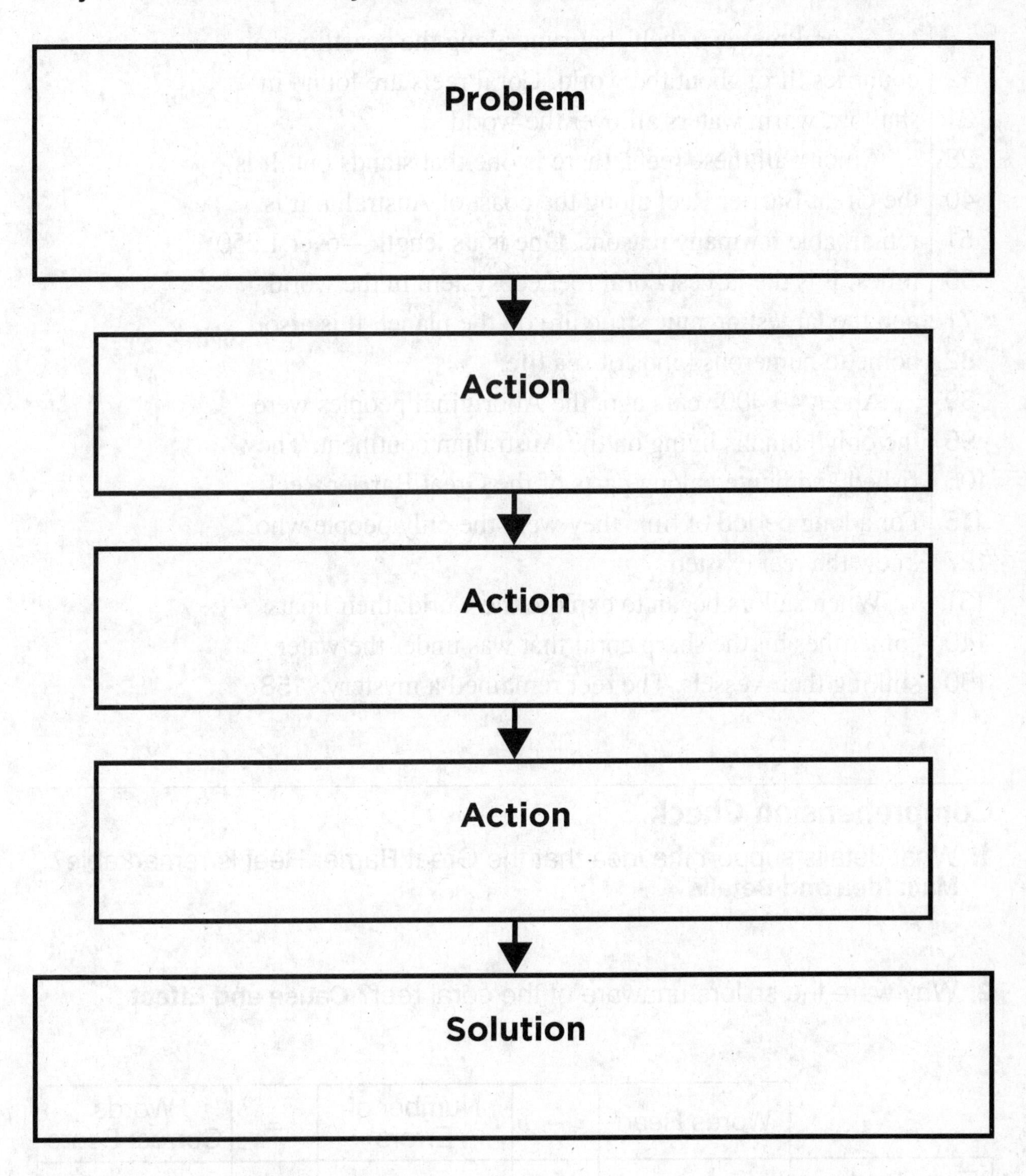

How does the information you wrote in the Problem and Solution Chart help you better understand *Leah's Pony*?

Name ______________________________

As I read, I will pay attention to reading with accuracy.

A coral reef is a shelf that runs along the coastlines of
12 countries throughout the world. Coral reefs are found in
21 shallow, warm waters all over the world.
28 Among all these reefs, there is one that stands out. It is
40 the Great Barrier Reef along the coast of Australia. It is
51 remarkable for many reasons. One is its length—over 1,250
60 miles. It is the largest coral reef ecosystem in the world,
71 and the largest organic structure on the planet. It is also
82 home to numerous kinds of sea life.
89 About 40,000 years ago, the Aboriginal peoples were
96 the only humans living on the Australian continent. They
105 fished and hunted along parts of the Great Barrier Reef.
115 For a long period of time they were the only people who
127 knew the reef existed.
131 When sailors began to explore the world, their boats
140 sometimes hit the sharp coral that was under the water,
150 sinking their vessels. The reef remained a mystery. 158

Comprehension Check

1. What details support the idea that the Great Barrier Reef is remarkable? **Main Idea and Details**

2. Why were the sailors unaware of the coral reef? **Cause and Effect**

	Words Read	–	Number of Errors	=	Words Correct Score
First Read		–		=	
Second Read		–		=	

R 1.1 Read narrative and expository text aloud with grade-appropriate fluency and accuracy and with appropriate pacing, intonation, and expression.

Name ______________________________

Primary sources are items from the past, such as photos, letters, and journals. They give us a firsthand understanding of earlier times.

November 14, 1914

Dear Diary,

Yesterday was my 9th birthday. To celebrate, Father took us for a ride in his new motor car. We drove to Mammoth Mountain. Because it was my birthday, Father let me crank the car and toot the horn.

We had a picnic lunch and enjoyed jam sandwiches. Next month is my brother Maxwell's birthday. I hope we get to go for another ride!

Emma

Use the journal entry and photo to answer the questions.

1. Who created this primary source? When was it created?

____

____

2. Why was this journal entry created?

____

3. What can a reader today learn from looking at this illustration of a photo?

____

____

4. What other sources could help you learn more about this time and place?

____

CA R 2.0 Reading Comprehension

Name ______________________________

Practice

Vocabulary Strategy: Unfamiliar Words

A dictionary can help you find the meanings of **unfamiliar words.**

Look at this dictionary entry for an unfamiliar word. Use the definition and sample sentence to help answer the questions that follow.

avid *adjective.* **1.** very eager. *She is an* avid *reader.*

1. What does *avid* mean, in your own words?

____

2. Use *avid* in another sentence.

____

3. How would you find the meaning of the word *incognito*?

____

4. Use a dictionary. Write the meaning of *incognito* below.

____

CA R 1.0 Word Analysis, Fluency, and Systematic Vocabulary Development

Name ______________________________

Using the Word Study Steps

1. LOOK at the word.
2. SAY the word aloud.
3. STUDY the letters in the word.
4. WRITE the word.
5. CHECK the word.
   Did you spell the word right?
   If not, go back to step 1.

End Game!

Find the word ending from the box below that completes each spelling word.

on	en	in

1. wov ____________
2. wag ____________
3. cous ____________
4. pengu ____________
5. prov ____________
6. reas ____________
7. butt ____________
8. wood ____________
9. bac ____________
10. ridd ____________
11. comm ____________
12. cott ____________
13. elev ____________
14. muff ____________
15. skelet ____________
16. wid ____________
17. oft ____________
18. sunk ____________
19. rob ____________
20. rais ____________

CA **LC 1.7** Spell correctly roots, inflections, suffixes and prefixes, and syllable constructions.

Name ________________________________

Practice

Spelling: *-in, -on, -en*

A. Proofreading Activity

There are six spelling mistakes in this poem. Circle the misspelled words. Write the words correctly on the lines below.

The Gold Rush Ghosts

Have you heard the tale of the lady
Who wears the cottin dress?
They offen say she's waiting,
And won't accept she's dead.
All day she sits on her woodun chair
Staring out to see
If her lover has riden by outside.
For someday his bride she'll be.

But her true love hasn't provin
That he's a rightful man.
He's still searching for a gold mine
Like every commen man.
So she still sits and he still rides,
These two unhappy souls.
She never will see her love
And he never will find gold.

1. ____________ 3. ____________ 5. ____________

2. ____________ 4. ____________ 6. ____________

B. Writing Activity

Write a poem of your own. Use at least three spelling words in your poem.

____

____

____

____

____

____

____

____

CA LC 1.7 Spell correctly roots, inflections, suffixes and prefixes, and syllable constructions.

Name ______________________________

- An **adverb** is a word that tells more about a verb.
- Some adverbs tell *how* an action takes place.
- Some adverbs tell *when* an action takes place.
- Some adverbs tell *where* an action takes place.

Underline the adverb in each sentence. Then write if the adverb tells *how*, *when*, or *where* the action takes place.

1. My mother and I went to the library together for information about our ancestors. ______________
2. Many Native Americans lived freely on this land. ______________
3. Tomorrow we will visit our local museum of natural history. ______________
4. Were they traveling far in search of gold? ______________
5. Did James Marshall first find gold at Sutter's Mill? ______________
6. John Sutter, Jr., built a new city nearby along the Sacramento River. ______________
7. We patiently sifted the sand for gold. ______________
8. Our uncle examined the rock carefully. ______________
9. He carelessly threw the stone back in the water. ______________
10. That greedy miner looked at them suspiciously. ______________
11. We quickly ran down the path. ______________
12. We then found the gold. ______________

CA **LC 1.3** Identify and use regular and irregular verbs, **adverbs**, prepositions, and coordinating conjunctions in writing and speaking.

Name ____________________

Practice

Grammar: Adverbs

- An **adverb** is a word that tells more about a verb.
- Some adverbs tell *how* an action takes place.
- Most adverbs that tell *how* end in ***-ly***. They are formed by adding ***-ly*** to an adjective.

A. Read the magazine article below, and circle the six incorrect adverbs. Then write the words correctly on the lines below.

When the gold miners of 1849 were looking for gold, they frequent found shiny stones in their pans. However, not all were true gold. Fool's gold, also called pyrite, is a stone that some miners mistaken confused with the real thing. What if you ever find a rock that looks like gold? These three ways can quick help you find out if it is real gold or fool's gold.

First, look careful at the color. Both are shiny and yellow-colored, but real gold also has a silver tone. The color of fool's gold is more like brass. Next, look at the shape. Fool's gold usual forms cubes and larger shapes. Real gold comes in chunks, flakes, or sheets. Last, brisk rub it against another hard object and smell it. Gold has no smell, but fool's gold will smell a little like rotten eggs. Maybe that's why they call it *fool's* gold!

1. ____________ 3. ____________ 5. ____________

2. ____________ 4. ____________ 6. ____________

B. Rewrite the above article with the correct adverbs on the lines.

____

____

____

____

____

CA **LC 1.3** Identify and use regular and irregular verbs, **adverbs**, prepositions, and coordinating conjunctions in writing and speaking.

Name ______________________

Practice

Writing: Character Growth: Believable

1. **Brainstorm** 3 things you did yesterday or today. These should be things you think other kids your age do sometimes too.

   Example: Got dressed

   1.

   2.

   3.

2. **Circle one** of the moments from your brainstorm.

3. **Think** about the moment you circled.

4. **List** 3 things you did or said in the moment you circled.

   Example: Couldn't find my sneakers

   1.

   2.

   3.

5. **Write** 3-5 sentences about a made-up kid doing the activity you described. What does the kid do and say in that moment?

____

____

____

____

____

____

____

____

CA W 1.0 Writing Strategies

Homophones are words that sound the same but are spelled differently and have different meanings. The words ***right*** and ***write*** are homophones.
right = correct   write = make marks on paper

Fill in each blank with the correct homophone.

1. **tale / tail** He told a ______________ about a lion that lost its ______________.
2. **patience / patients** The doctor encouraged his ______________ to have more ______________ while they waited to see him.
3. **dough / doe** The ______________ and her fawns ate the ______________ that the baker left on the window sill.
4. **wade / weighed** She tried to ______________ across the river wearing a backpack that ______________ 90 pounds.
5. **bolder / boulder** The skier grew ______________ after he jumped over the ______________.
6. **plain / plane** We flew in a ______________ over the ______________ where the buffalo were.
7. **week / weak** I felt ______________ for a ______________.
8. **aloud / allowed** "There are no photos ______________," the guide said ______________.

Name ______________________________

annoyed	circular	outstretched
conducted	reference	disappointment

A. Draw a line to match the vocabulary word to its meaning.

1. reference
2. disappointment
3. annoyed
4. circular
5. outstretched
6. conducted

a. reaching out
b. led
c. round, like a circle
d. upset
e. the feeling when something doesn't happen the way you hoped it would
f. a source of reliable information

B. Write a paragraph or two using as many of the vocabulary words as possible.

____

____

____

____

____

____

____

____

____

CA R 1.0 Word Analysis, Fluency, and Systematic Vocabulary Development

Name ______________________________

A **cause** is what makes something happen. If you can answer the question "Why did that happen?" then you know the cause.

What happens as a result of the cause is the **effect**. If you can answer the question "What happened?" then you know the effect.

Read the passage below. As you read, think about causes and effects. Then answer the questions.

Sam Brannan was a merchant in San Francisco. When he heard that gold had been found near the American River, he knew just what to do. He bought up every pickax, shovel, and pan in the entire city. Then he ran through the streets of San Francisco spreading the news about the discovery of gold.

Because Brannan was the only merchant who had tools to sell, he could charge as much as he wanted. Prospectors were willing to spend $15.00 for a pan that was worth only 60 cents. It wasn't long before Brannan became one of the richest men in California—without ever panning for gold!

1. What caused Sam Brannan to buy up all the mining tools?

____

2. What was the effect of Brannan's spreading the news about gold?

____

3. What caused miners to pay $15.00 for a 60-cent pan? ______________

____

4. What was the effect of so many prospectors buying Brannan's tools?

____

R 2.1 Identify structural patterns found in informational text (e.g., compare and contrast, cause and effect, sequential or chronological order, proposition and support) to strengthen comprehension.

Name ______________________________

As you read *The Gold Rush Game*, fill in the Cause and Effect Diagram.

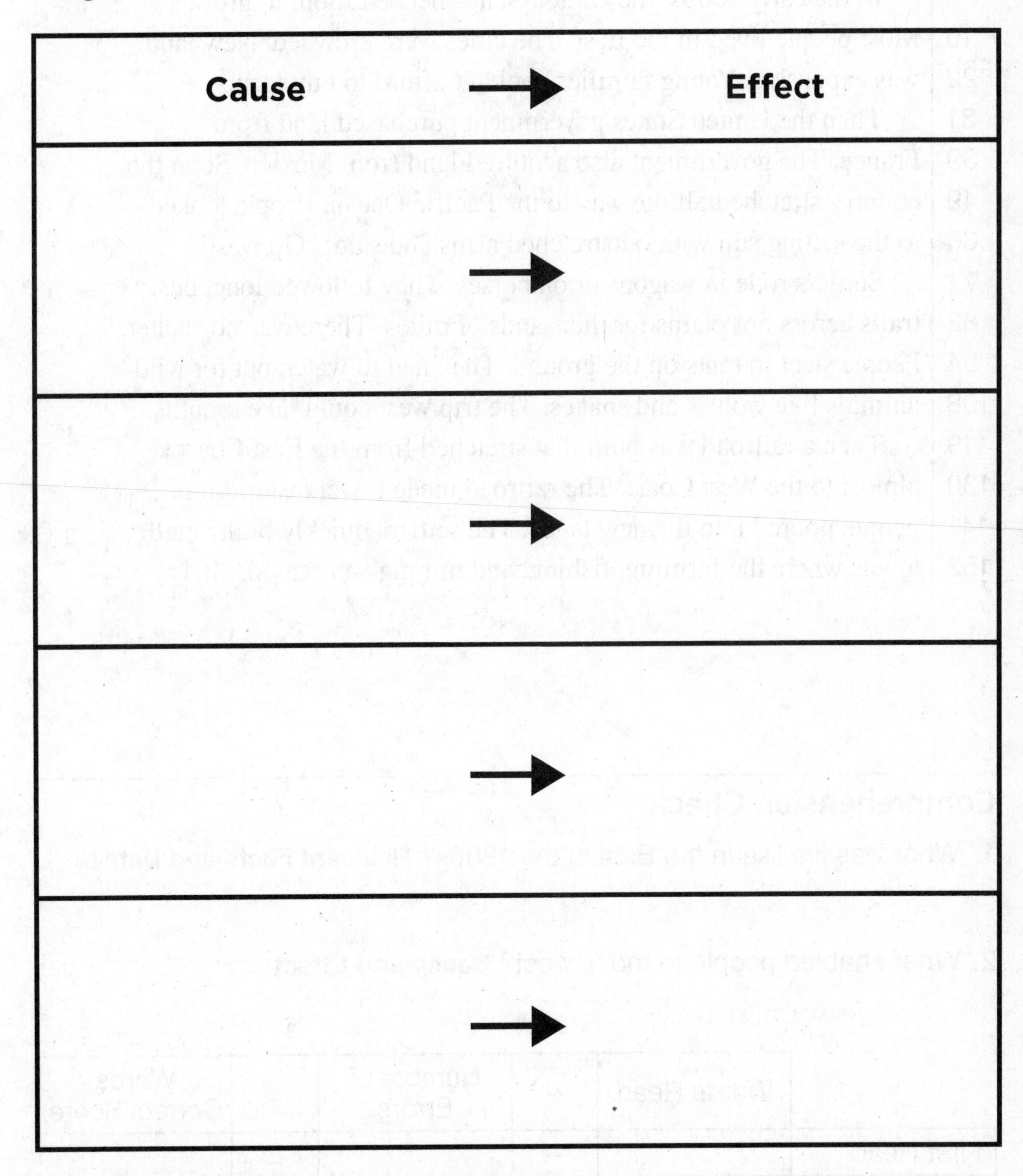

How does the information you wrote in the Cause and Effect Diagram help you to analyze the story structure of *The Gold Rush Game*?

R 2.1 Identify structural patterns found in informational text (e.g., compare and contrast, cause and effect, sequential or chronological order, proposition and support) to strengthen comprehension.

As I read, I will pay attention to intonation.

	In the early 1800s, the United States needed room to grow.
10	Most people lived in the East. The cities were crowded. New land
22	was expensive. Young families couldn't afford to buy farms.
31	Then the United States government purchased land from
39	France. The government also acquired land from Mexico. Soon the
49	country stretched all the way to the Pacific Ocean. People looked
60	to the setting sun with outstretched arms and said, "Go west!"
71	Settlers rode in wagons or on horses. They followed long, dusty
82	trails across hot plains for thousands of miles. There was no shelter.
94	People slept in tents on the ground. They had to watch out for wild
108	animals like wolves and snakes. The trip west could take months.
119	Then a railroad was built that stretched from the East Coast
130	almost to the West Coast. The railroad made travel faster. More
141	people poured into the new lands. The settlers quickly built small
152	towns where the farming, fishing, and mining were good. 161

Comprehension Check

1. What was life like in the East in the 1800s? **Relevant Facts and Details**

2. What enabled people to move west? **Cause and Effect**

	Words Read	–	Number of Errors	=	Words Correct Score
First Read		–		=	
Second Read		–		=	

CA **R 1.1** Read narrative and expository text aloud with grade-appropriate fluency and accuracy and with appropriate pacing, intonation, and expression.

Name ___________________________

Practice

Text Feature: Time Line

A **time line** is a visual way to show a sequence of historical events in a period of time. A time line can be vertical or horizontal. It contains a title, dates, and events. Events are shown on the time line in the order in which they happened, and sometimes the events are illustrated.

Use the time line to answer the questions.

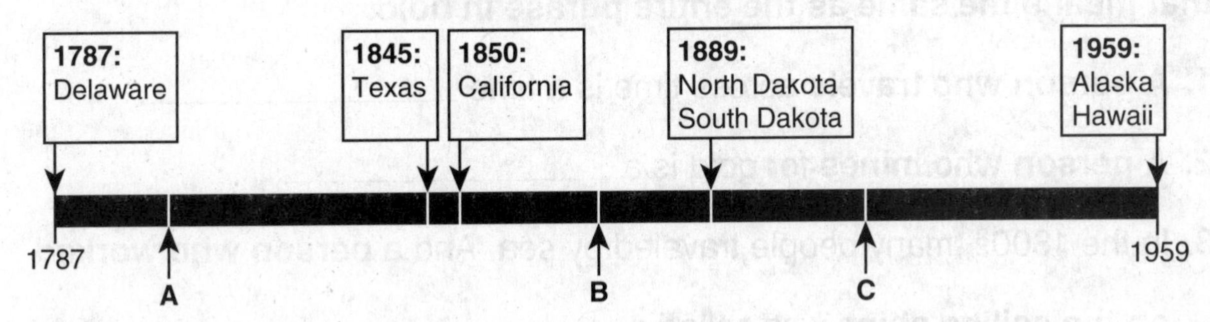

1. What is the subject of the time line?

____

____

2. When did California become a state? ___________

3. Which states became states in 1889? ___________________

____

4. How many years does the time line cover? ___________

5. Arizona and New Mexico became states in 1912. Where would you put that event on the time line—at point A, point B, or point C? ___________

6. What is the earliest date on this time line? The latest date? ___________

Name ______________________________

A **suffix** is a word part that can be added to the end of a base word. Adding a suffix to a base word changes its meaning. When added to the end of a verb, the suffix *-er* or *-or* means "a person who."

teach + er = teacher (a person who teaches)
act + or = actor (a person who acts)

Look for the verb. Then add the correct suffix to make a word that means the same as the entire phrase in bold.

1. **A person who travels** across time is a time ______________.
2. **A person who mines** for gold is a ______________.
3. In the 1800s, many people traveled by sea. And **a person who worked on the sailing ships** was called a ______________.
4. Wong Daido was **a person who survived** the river current. He was a ______________.
5. **A person who settled** in California was a ______________.
6. **A person who bikes** on California's mountain trails is a mountain ______________.
7. **A person who visits** the site of Sutter's Mill is a ______________.
8. **A person who researches** the history of the California Gold Rush is a ______________.

Name ______________________________

Using the Word Study Steps

1. LOOK at the word.
2. SAY the word aloud.
3. STUDY the letters in the word.
4. WRITE the word.
5. CHECK the word.
   Did you spell the word right?
   If not, go back to step 1.

Find and Circle

Find and circle the 20 spelling words.

P	D	P	Z	R	Q	M	W	H	O	'	S
R	O	R	T	O	B	O	U	L	D	E	R
I	U	I	A	U	M	O	U	S	S	E	W
N	G	N	L	T	G	S	V	J	W	K	X
T	H	C	E	E	Z	E	W	B	A	J	P
S	Z	E	H	Q	P	V	C	B	D	Y	A
T	G	G	C	P	Z	J	D	O	E	T	T
R	W	H	V	Q	B	K	W	L	B	A	I
'	B	W	E	I	G	H	E	D	M	I	E
J	W	H	O	S	E	K	'	E	Y	L	N
F	W	E	A	V	E	P	V	R	O	O	T
P	A	T	I	E	N	C	E	R	'	J	S

CA LC 1.7 Spell correctly roots, inflections, suffixes and prefixes, and syllable constructions.

Name ______________________________

Practice

Spelling: Homophones

A. Proofreading

There are six spelling mistakes in this story. Circle the misspelled words. Write the words correctly on the lines below.

A Tael of the Two Deer

Once upon a time, there was a dou named Cinnamon. Cinnamon lived in a grand kingdom with all of her animal friends. Cinnamon was also very much in love with Printse Butternut. But Cinnamon and Butternut were very upset. Their kingdom was in danger. Nearby was a large human city. Every year the humans would build another road or roote closer to their kingdom. If a deer heard a car coming he would raise his taile to warn the other animals. Then one day, Cinnamon and Butternut had an idea. They got all the other animals in the kingdom to help them. Bowlder upon rock, the animals built a wall that would protect them from the cars on the roads. Cinnamon hoped that all the animals would be very careful and not cross the wall. That way the kingdom would remain safe.

1. ______________ 3. ______________ 5. ______________

2. ______________ 4. ______________ 6. ______________

B. Writing Activity

Write a story about animals interacting with humans. Use at least three spelling words in your paragraph.

____

____

____

____

____

____

CA **LC 1.7** Spell correctly roots, inflections, suffixes and prefixes, and syllable constructions.

Name ______________________________

- Use *more* or *most* to form comparisons with adverbs that end in *-ly* or with longer adverbs.
- Use *more* to compare two actions.
- Use *most* to compare more than two actions.
- When you use *more* or *most*, do not use the ending *-er* or *-est*.

Use *more* or *most* with the underlined adverb in each first sentence to complete the two sentences that follow.

1. The train that Chester was on shook harshly as it moved on the track.

   The second train shook ______________ every now and then.

   But the subway car shook ______________ of all.

2. Chester furiously tried to escape from the picnic basket.

   He tried ______________ as the train rattled and shook.

   Chester tried the ______________ of all when they finally reached New York.

3. Harry Cat speedily jumped toward Chester and Tucker Mouse.

   Chester jumped the ______________ of all into the matchbox.

   Chester jumped ______________ than Harry Cat.

4. Chester chirps sweetly when he is excited.

   Chester chirps ______________ when he is scared.

   But Chester chirps the ______________ when he is happy.

5. Chester moves hastily through the drain pipe.

   Harry Cat moves ______________ through the drain pipe.

   But Tucker moves the ______________ of all through the drain pipe.

CA **LC 1.3** Identify and use regular and irregular verbs, adverbs, prepositions, and coordinating conjunctions in writing and speaking.

Name ______________________________

A. Read the magazine article below and circle six incorrect uses of adverbs.

Last week, a baby bird was lucky found in a nest near school. It sad seems that the bird got lost when its family went south. The bird was not used to the cold weather, so it hid inside the nest. Then a young boy and his uncle heard her chirping frantic up in the tree.

They took the baby bird to the animal hospital. The doctor there kind offered to take the bird to the zoo. At the zoo, the workers are taking good care of her. She is feeling much better now. As soon as she gets complete well, the zoo will send her south to be with other birds. She will happy be in a warmer climate.

B. Rewrite the above article with the correct adverbs on the lines below.

____

____

____

____

____

____

____

____

____

____

____

____

CA LC 1.3 Identify and use regular and irregular verbs, adverbs, prepositions, and coordinating conjunctions in writing and speaking.

Name ____

Drill 3: Character's Sense of Humor

1. **Read:**

   Steven was caught completely off guard by what he saw. It was the funniest thing he'd seen all year.

2. **Write** 2–3 more sentences that show what Steven saw and how he reacted in this moment.

____

____

____

____

____

____

____

____

____

____

____

____

____

____

____

____

Name ______________________________

When added to the beginning of a word, a prefix changes the meaning of the word.
The prefixes ***un-***, ***non-***, and ***dis-*** mean "not" or "the opposite of."

- **dis +** trust = distrust   to not trust
- **non +** sense = nonsense   something that doesn't make sense
- **un +** covered = uncovered   the opposite of covered

The prefix ***mis-*** means "badly" or "incorrectly."

- **mis +** spell = misspell   to spell incorrectly

Each of these prefixes has a short vowel sound.

Underline the prefix in the following words. Then write the meaning of the word.

1. disobey ______________________________

2. unsure ______________________________

3. misbehave ______________________________

4. nonsense ______________________________

5. unhappy ______________________________

6. dislike ______________________________

7. misunderstand ______________________________

8. disconnect ______________________________

9. unbelievable ______________________________

10. miscalculate ______________________________

Name ______________________________

A. Complete the story by filling in the blanks with vocabulary words.

decades	active	transform	volunteer	violated

Shawn is a ________________ at his community's recreation center. He noticed that some of the playground equipment hadn't been replaced in ________________. He suggested a fundraiser to raise money for new equipment. Then he took an ________________ role in planning a talent show. When the new equipment arrived, Shawn was excited because he knew it would ________________ the recreation center. Now he supervises younger children on the equipment to make sure safety rules aren't ________________.

B. Write two sentences about a way you would like to help in your community. Use a vocabulary word in each sentence. Underline the words that you use.

____

____

____

____

____

____

____

____

Name ______________________________

A **generalization** is a broad statement that applies to a variety of people or situations.

- To make a generalization, combine text information with your own knowledge and experience.
- Words such as *none*, *always*, *usually*, and *many* can signal generalizations.

A. Read the paragraph. Then read the questions and circle the letter next to the correct answer.

After Juanita's grandfather died, she noticed that her grandmother seemed lonely. Like most people, Juanita's grandmother was looking for friendship and someone to talk to. Juanita thought other older people might also need companionship.

Juanita organized Sponsor-a-Senior at her school. She matched students with patients at a nearby senior center. The students called their seniors, visited them, and made them cards.

1. Which of the following is a generalization?

a. Juanita organized Sponsor-a-Senior at her school.

b. Like most people, Juanita's grandmother was looking for friendship and someone to talk to.

2. Read your answer to question 1. Which word makes it a generalization?

a. organized

b. most

B. Read the sentence. Write a generalization based on it.

3. There are 30 students in Juanita's class. Twenty-seven students volunteered to help at the senior center. ______________________________

____

Name ______________________________

As you read *Taking the Lead*, fill in the Make Generalizations Chart.

Important Information	Generalization

How does the information you wrote in your Make Generalizations Chart help you understand and evaluate the information in *Taking the Lead*?

Practice

Fluency: Expression

Name ______________________________

As I read, I will pay attention to expression.

	Thousands of years ago, pharaohs ruled the great kingdom
9	of Egypt. When pharaohs died, they were buried in tombs
19	with their treasures. One of these pharaohs was very young.
29	His name was King Tutankhamen (TOOT-ahngk-ah-muhn).
34	The entrance to Tutankhamen's tomb was well hidden.
42	The Egyptians built tombs that were hard to find and even
53	harder to enter. They made secret entrances and false passages.
63	Soon after the king was buried, robbers broke into the
73	tomb and took some of the treasures. The tomb was then
84	resealed. It stayed buried in the sand for thousands of years.
95	In the early 1900s, an Englishman named Lord Carnarvon
103	began the search for this pharoah's tomb. Carnarvon believed
112	that the king was buried in the Valley of the Kings.
123	In 1907, Carnarvon began working with a man named
131	Howard Carter. Carter was an artist for paleontologists.
139	He made drawings of the fossils and other findings. Carter
149	and Carnarvon began a search for King Tutankhamen's
157	tomb. It was a search that would last for many years. 168

Comprehension Check

1. How do you know that King Tutankhamen's tomb was hard to find? **Relevant Facts and Details**

2. Why did the Egyptians build tombs that were hard to find? **Cause and Effect**

	Words Read	–	Number of Errors	=	Words Correct Score
First Read		–		=	
Second Read		–		=	

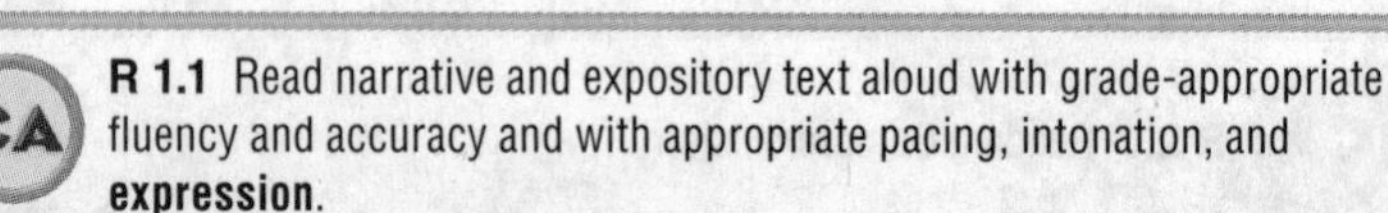

R 1.1 Read narrative and expository text aloud with grade-appropriate fluency and accuracy and with appropriate pacing, intonation, and **expression**.

Name ______________________________

For items 1–12, read the passage and fill in the information asked for in the form. Then answer the questions that follow.

Mr. Carter's fourth-grade class plans to visit the York Science Museum on Friday, April 22. The bus will leave at 8:00 A.M. and return at 4:00 P.M. Students should bring a bag lunch on the day of the trip. Permission forms must be returned to Mr. Carter by Friday, April 8.

Field Trip Permission Form

1. Student's Name ______________ 2. Date of trip __________
3. Student's Address ______________________

   ____
4. Home Phone # ______________________
5. Destination ______________________
6. Transportation by ☐ Bus ☐ Car ☐ Subway
7. Time Departing ____________ 8. Time Returning ____________
9. Parent's Name ______________________
10. ☐ I give permission for my son/daughter to go.
11. Parent's Signature ______________________
12. Today's Date ______________________

13. Should the student write in the space next to item 11 on the form? Explain why.

____

14. What is the latest date that should appear in the space next to item 12?

____

Name ______________________________

Sequence Writing Frame

A. Summarize *Taking the Lead*.
Use the Sequence Writing Frame below.

Dolores Huerta is an important leader in the Latin community.

After college, Dolores Huerta ______________________________
____
______________________________.

In 1955, she ______________________________
____
______________________________.

In 1962, she teamed up with ______________________________ to
____
____
______________________________.

Over the years, she ______________________________
____
______________________________.

Today, Dolores Huerta ______________________________
____
______________________________.

Dolores Huerta has changed the lives of many people throughout California and beyond.

B. Rewrite the completed summary on another sheet of paper. Keep it as a model for writing a summary of an article or selection using this text structure.

CA R 2.0 Reading Comprehension

Name ______________________________

Many English words are formed by adding word parts, such as prefixes and suffixes, to a basic word, or root word. Many words have roots that come from Latin, the language of ancient Rome, or Greek, the language of Greece.

- Words that have the root *loc* have to do with a place.
- Words that have the root *phon* have to do with sound.
- Words that have the root *graph* have to do with writing.

Complete each sentence with a word from the box that can take the place of the underlined words.

graphic	relocate	location	telephone	biography

1. The committee met to choose a place for the new community center. ______________
2. Lee included a diagram in her report to illustrate one of the ideas she wrote about. ______________
3. One way people communicate is by calling one another on a device that transmits sound. ______________
4. Some people move to a different place when there is a war in their homeland. ______________
5. I read a written account of the life of César Chávez. ______________

CA **R 1.4** Know common roots and affixes derived from Greek and Latin and use this knowledge to analyze the meaning of complex words (e.g., *international*).

Name ______________________________

Using the Word Study Steps

1. LOOK at the word.
2. SAY the word aloud.
3. STUDY the letters in the word.
4. WRITE the word.
5. CHECK the word.
   Did you spell the word right?
   If not, go back to step 1.

X the Word

Put an X on the word that does not have the same prefix as the spelling word on the left.

1. discourage	disk	disrespect
2. mislabel	misinform	misty
3. nonsense	none	nonviolent
4. unplug	untold	under
5. distrust	dish	dislike
6. misnumber	misses	mistake
7. uncover	unite	unfold
8. disappoint	dime	disappear
9. nonfiction	nondairy	noon
10. misstep	mice	misbehave
11. unable	unlucky	unit
12. disbelief	different	disable
13. misplace	mild	misplay
14. uncomfortable	uniform	unaware
15. nonfat	nonstick	noodle

CA LC 1.7 Spell correctly roots, inflections, suffixes and prefixes, and syllable constructions.

Name ______________________________

A. Proofreading

There are six spelling mistakes in this letter. Circle the misspelled words. Write the words correctly on the lines below.

Dear Grandma,

I just got back from the dinosaur museum! I was unsertan about how much I would learn there, but it did not dissapoint me.

When we walked into the T. rex exhibit, I was unabell to talk. That was one huge dinosaur! We read the sign about how the scientists uncuvar the fossils very carefully.

We made only one mistepp. We did not get there early enough. The museum closed before we were done, even though we were going nonnstop the whole time. Mom promised we could go back soon. Maybe you could come, too!

Love,
Yoli

1. ____________ 3. ____________ 5. ____________

2. ____________ 4. ____________ 6. ____________

B. Writing Activity

Imagine that you are a scientist who studies animals or plants through fossils. Write an e-mail to a co-worker about something you have found. Use at least four spelling words in your e-mail.

____

____

____

____

____

____

CA **LC 1.7** Spell correctly roots, inflections, suffixes and prefixes, and syllable constructions.

Name ______________________

- You can correct a sentence with two **negatives** by changing one negative to a positive word.

no—any	nothing—anything	no one—anyone
never—ever	nobody—anybody	nowhere—anywhere

Correct these sentences by changing one negative word to a positive word.

1. Hakeem never wanted nothing to do with science.

____

2. He didn't like to be nowhere near dirt and bones.

____

3. His teacher thought he wouldn't never pass her class.

____

4. There wasn't nobody who disliked science more than he did.

____

____

5. Hakeem hadn't never seen anything like that piece of amber.

____

____

6. Now there isn't no class more fun than science.

____

7. Hakeem isn't never late for class anymore.

____

8. There isn't no better way to thank her for what she did.

____

____

CA LC 1.0 Written and Oral English Language Conventions

Name ___________________________

A. Read the personal essay below. Underline the sentences that contain two negatives.

The New Kid in Class

Last month, I started going to a new school. I didn't know nobody at this school. At first, I thought there wasn't no way I would be comfortable here.

The teacher introduced me to the class. I had to tell them a little about myself. Everyone was laughing at me. I didn't have no idea what to say. I told the class about how I'd seen a real bear far off in the woods.

Instead of laughing at me, the students were all listening to me. They asked me lots of questions. I still don't know if I'll get used to this new school, but my first day didn't turn out so bad.

B. Rewrite the personal essay, correcting the sentences that contain two negatives.

____

____

____

____

____

____

____

____

____

____

____

Writing Rubric

4 Excellent	3 Good	2 Fair	1 Unsatisfactory
Ideas and Content/ Genre	Ideas and Content/ Genre	Ideas and Content/ Genre	Ideas and Content/ Genre
Organization and Focus	Organization and Focus	Organization and Focus	Organization and Focus
Sentence Structure/ Fluency	Sentence Structure/ Fluency	Sentence Structure/ Fluency	Sentence Structure/ Fluency
Conventions	Conventions	Conventions	Conventions
Word Choice	Word Choice	Word Choice	Word Choice
Voice	Voice	Voice	Voice
Presentation	Presentation	Presentation	Presentation

Name ______________________________

Suffixes are word endings that change the meaning of a base word.
The suffixes ***-y*** and ***-ful*** mean "full of."
dirty = full of dirt joyful = full of joy
The suffix ***-ly*** *means* "in a certain way."
nicely = in a nice way
The suffix ***-less*** *means* "without."
breathless = without breath
The suffix ***-ness*** means "the state of being."
sickness = the state of being sick

Circle the suffix in each word. Then circle the correct meaning of the word.

1. cloudy
a. full of clouds **b.** without clouds **c.** in a clouded way

2. suddenly
a. full of sudden **b.** the opposite of sudden **c.** in a sudden way

3. powerful
a. without power **b.** the state of being powered by **c.** full of power

4. shoeless
a. full of shoes **b.** without shoes **c.** the state of having shoes

5. kindness
a. the state of being kind **b.** full of kind **c.** without any kind

6. loudly
a. without loud **b.** full of loud **c.** in a loud way

Name ______________________________

A. Choose a word in the box to replace the underlined word or words in each sentence.

technique	foolishness	inspire
evaporate	magnify	annual

1. Lucky for him, Bentley's mother never said, "Stop this silliness! Come in out of the storm at once!" ______________

2. Bentley had to develop a special method to photograph snowflakes.

   ____

3. The newspaper held an occurring-every-year photo contest.

   ____

4. Bentley had to work fast to make sure a snowflake didn't dry up. ______________

B. Use each word correctly in a sentence.

5. magnify ____

   ____

6. inspire ____

   ____

CA R 1.0 Word Analysis, Fluency, and Systematic Vocabulary Development

Name ______________________________

To **draw a conclusion**, use information from the selection and your own knowledge and experience with a similar situation.

Read the passage. Then read the conclusions. Support each one with information from the story.

Ramón's science project was due on Wednesday, but things had not gone as planned. He was trying to train his dog, Snowball, not to bark when someone came through the door. He had thought that giving Snowball a treat when she stopped barking would teach her to sit quietly. He'd repeated the procedure each day for two weeks and recorded the results. Snowball was still barking.

Ramón talked to his teacher, Mrs. Gomez, about his problem. "Hmm," she said. "From what you've written in your notebook, it looks like the two times when Snowball did sit quietly, you also used a firm voice and patted her head." "You're right!" Ramón exclaimed. "I know exactly what to do."

On Wednesday, the students in Mrs. Gomez's class turned in their reports. Ramón was last. "Thanks for your help, Mrs. Gomez," Ramón said. "I guess in science, just like everything else, it's really important to keep on trying."

1. Ramón's dog Snowball sometimes misbehaves. ______________________________

____

2. Ramón would like to improve Snowball's behavior. ______________________________

____

____

3. Ramón's experiment fails. ______________________________

____

4. Ramón is concerned about his science experiment. ______________________________

____

CA **R 2.4** Evaluate new information and hypotheses by testing them against known information and ideas.

Name ______________________________

As you read *Snowflake Bentley*, fill in the Conclusions Chart.

Text Clues	Conclusion

How does the information you wrote in your Conclusions Chart help you better understand *Snowflake Bentley*?

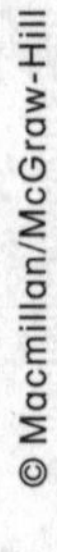

CA **R 2.4** Evaluate new information and hypotheses by testing them against known information and ideas.

Name ______________________

As I read, I will pay attention to the pronunciation of vocabulary words.

Tornadoes begin with warm, humid air. Humid air is air
10 that holds a lot of moisture. This humid air meets up with
22 colder air. As the air masses come together, the warm air
33 rises. As the warm air moves upward, it holds more and
44 more moisture. Huge, dark clouds called thunderheads begin
52 to develop. These clouds can spread as wide as 100 miles
62 (161 km) across the sky. There is so much moisture in the
73 clouds that it can't just **evaporate** into the air. So it falls as
86 rain. The thunderheads produce giant storms with thunder
94 and lightning. These storms are called supercells.
101 Winds high up in the storm clouds blow faster than the
112 winds lower down. The winds also blow in different
121 directions. This causes the air to spin. Then, as the winds
132 spin, they form a long funnel cloud. However, one last
142 thing needs to happen for the funnel cloud to become a
153 tornado. It needs to touch the ground. 160

Comprehension Check

1. Describe the conditions needed to form a thunderhead. **Main Ideas and Details**

2. What is the author's purpose? **Author's Purpose**

	Words Read	–	Number of Errors	=	Words Correct Score
First Read		–		=	
Second Read		–		=	

CA **R 1.1** Read narrative and expository text aloud with grade-appropriate fluency and accuracy and with appropriate pacing, intonation, and expression.

Name ______________________________

Practice

Literary Element: Imagery and Figurative Language

Imagery is the use of words to create a picture in the reader's mind.
Figurative language uses words differently from their usual meaning.

Read each haiku and answer the questions that follow.

This light rain falling
Tickles my skin like feathers.
A hot bath calls me.

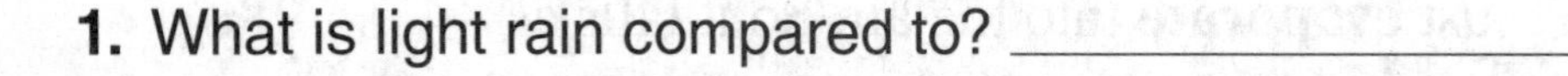

1. What is light rain compared to? ______________

2. Can a hot bath really call someone? What does this mean?

____

____

Sun after gray days,
Like Fourth of July fireworks,
Bursts forth bright with joy.

3. What is the sun compared to? ______________

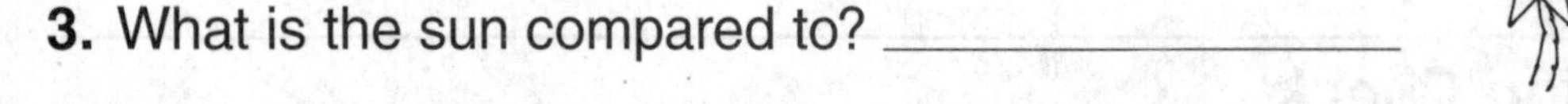

4. What figurative language is used in the poem? How can you tell?

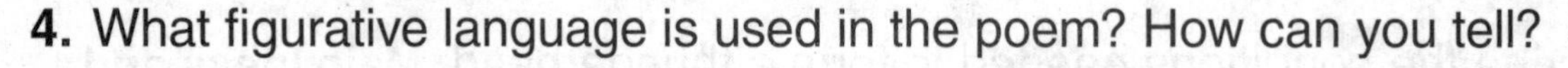

____

A summer hailstorm—
Daisies burrow underground.
They're not meant for ice!

5. What words in this haiku describe something that could not happen?

____

CA **R 3.5** Define figurative language (e.g., simile, metaphor, hyperbole, personification) and identify its use in literary works.

Name ________________________________

Multiple-meaning words are words that have more than one meaning. You can use the dictionary to find the correct meaning.

pick *verb* **1.** to select or choose. Pick *a card from the deck.* **2.** to gather with the fingers. *We* picked *blueberries for a pie.* **3.** to pull at and let go; pluck. *She* picked *the strings on the banjo.* *noun* **1.** a tool with a wooden handle and a metal head, used for breaking rocks and loosening dirt. *He used a* pick *to break the rocks into chunks.* **2.** a thin piece of metal or plastic used for playing a stringed instrument. *I bought a new* pick *at the guitar shop.* **3.** the best of something. *Take your* pick *of the books on the table.*

Use the dictionary entry above to answer the questions.

1. Pick one: playing in the snow or jumping in rain puddles.

Is *pick* a noun or a verb? ____________ Write the definition.

____

2. The gold miner's pick was worn down from breaking rocks.

Is *pick* a noun or a verb? ____________ What is the meaning of *pick* in this sentence? ________________________________

3. Did you pick enough blueberries for a pie?

Is *pick* a noun or a verb? ____________ Write the definition.

____

4. I strum the guitar with a pick.

Is *pick* a noun or a verb? ____________ Write the definition.

____

____

CA **R 1.6** Distinguish and interpret words with multiple meanings.

Name ______________________________

Using the Word Study Steps

1. LOOK at the word.
2. SAY the word aloud.
3. STUDY the letters in the word.
4. WRITE the word.
5. CHECK the word.
   Did you spell the word right?
   If not, go back to step 1.

Find and Circle

Find and circle the hidden spelling words.

H	A	P	P	I	N	E	S	S	X	Z	W	Q	Z
A	I	M	L	E	S	S	U	O	Z	T	D	X	J
N	B	A	R	E	L	Y	N	R	Q	A	C	Q	O
D	X	R	K	Y	Z	X	N	R	I	S	E	D	Y
F	G	E	N	T	L	Y	Y	O	L	T	R	S	F
U	W	Z	Q	K	Z	Q	K	W	L	E	T	I	U
L	I	F	E	L	E	S	S	F	N	L	A	C	L
H	P	P	E	E	U	L	W	U	E	E	I	K	L
A	Z	W	J	Y	Y	F	O	L	S	S	N	N	Y
I	B	R	E	A	T	H	L	E	S	S	L	E	B
R	F	U	R	R	Y	R	E	A	L	L	Y	S	N
Y	K	X	X	Z	G	O	O	D	N	E	S	S	C
A	H	O	P	E	F	U	L	L	Y	S	Y	L	Z

CA LC 1.7 Spell correctly roots, inflections, suffixes and prefixes, and syllable constructions.

Name ______________________________

A. Proofreading

There are five spelling mistakes in these paragraphs. Circle the misspelled words. Write the words correctly on the lines below.

I realie love to build paper airplanes. My best friend and I make a bunch of them and pretend we are the Wright brothers, preparing for the very first airplane flight. We fold and cut each plane until it is perfect.

We wait for a suny, windy afternoon and take our handfull of planes to the park. We try each plane, one after the other, to see which one flies the farthest. We race to the other end of the park to see which plane won. We are brethles when we get there.

I am always hoping that one of my planes will be the winner. I feel such happyness when that happens.

1. ______________ 3. ______________ 5. ______________

2. ______________ 4. ______________

B. Writing Activity

Imagine that you are an inventor. Write a short paragraph about your latest invention. Use at least three spelling words in your description.

____

____

____

____

____

____

____

____

CA **LC 1.7** Spell correctly roots, inflections, suffixes and prefixes, and syllable constructions.

Name ___________________________

A **prepositional phrase** is a group of words that begins with a **preposition** and ends with a noun or pronoun.

Underline the prepositional phrases in the following sentences.

1. When they finished their first plane, Orv and Katherine went on a camping trip.
2. Will flew the plane over a group of boys.
3. Katherine helped her brothers by managing their shop.
4. In their letters, they told her everything they were doing.
5. Will said that Kitty Hawk was a safe place for practice.
6. The world had never before seen a craft fly in the air.
7. First, they controlled their aircraft from the ground.
8. They came home to Dayton with a new idea.
9. Orv and Will worked from day to night.
10. They had their friend Charlie build an engine for their new aircraft.
11. "It could not be assembled in our shop."
12. The first flight of the *Flyer* was made by Will.
13. They wrote ideas on paper.
14. The brothers rode into town.
15. People flocked to the field.
16. The flights were printed in the newspapers.

Name ______________________________

Read the interview below. Then rewrite each line by switching the preposition in each underlined phrase with the correct one from another sentence.

1. "Captain Reilly, what do you like most inside exploring space?"

____

____

2. "I like the feeling that I am about another world. It's exciting."

____

____

3. "What is your job to the space shuttle?"

____

4. "I help the other crew members with repairs from the ship."

____

____

5. "What can kids learn for exploring space?"

____

6. "Exploring space can help kids above their science and math classes."

____

____

7. "Do you have any advice in our audience?"

____

8. "Yes. There is a whole world with you, kids. Discover it!"

____

____

CA LC 1.0 Written and Oral English Language Conventions

Name ______________________________

Practice

Writing: Character Development: Change in Behavior

1. The best way to tell that someone has changed or grown is to look at how they act. Think of a thing or activity that you used to *not* like but like now. Write it on the line. ______________________

2. Write 2–3 sentences showing what you did or said when you *didn't* like the thing or activity.

3. Write 2–3 sentences showing what you do or say now that you *do* like the thing or activity.

CA W 1.0 Writing Strategies

Name ______________________________

A **prefix** is a word part that can be added to the beginning of a base word and changes its meaning. The prefixes ***dis-***, ***non-***, and ***un-*** mean "the opposite of" or "without." The prefix ***mis-*** means "badly" or "incorrectly."

A. Underline the prefix in the following words. Then write the meaning of the word.

1. unusual ______________________

2. discontent ______________________

3. misread ______________________

4. nonsense ______________________

5. unafraid ______________________

A **suffix** is a word part that can be added to the end of a base word. Adding a suffix changes the meaning of the base word.

-y and ***-ful*** mean "full of" ***-ly*** means "in a certain way"

-less means "without" ***-ness*** means "the state of being"

B. Circle the suffix in each word. Then write the meaning of the word.

6. joyful ____________________

7. sadness ____________________

8. quietly ____________________

9. toothless ____________________

10. speedy ____________________

Name ______________________________

hilarious	dizzy	nowadays
handy	mischief	independence

Fill in the sentences below with words from the box. Then use the words in the blanks to complete the puzzle.

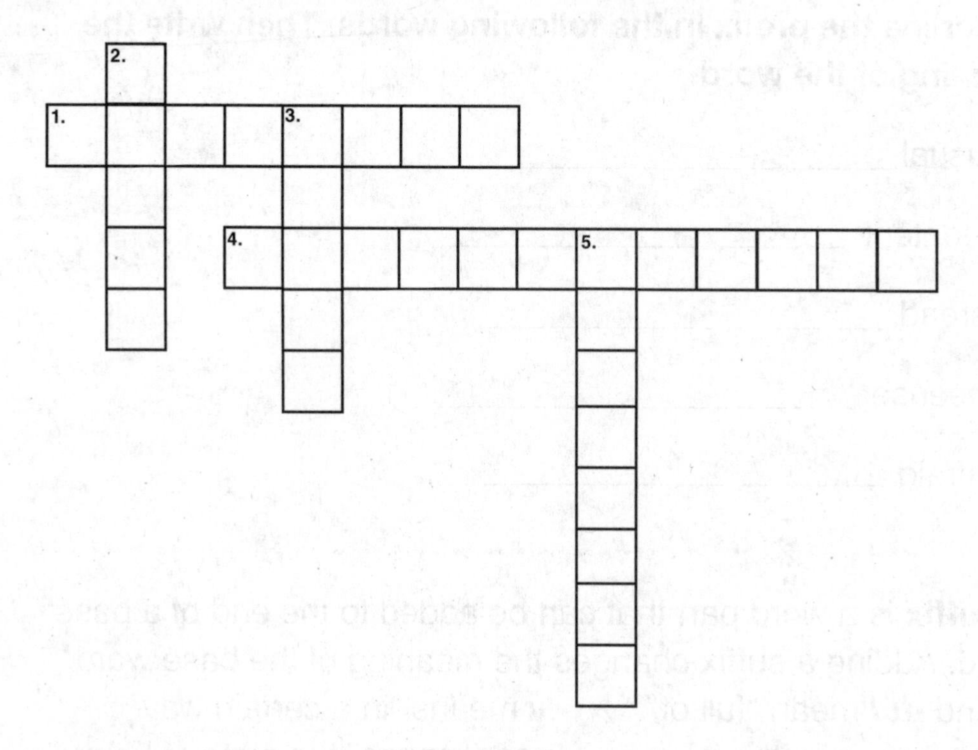

1. I never get into ______________ when I'm inventing something!
2. But when success goes to my head, I feel ______________!
3. My next invention will come in ______________ for senior citizens who live alone.
4. It will let them keep their ______________.
5. All I do ______________ is come up with bright ideas!

CA R 1.0 Word Analysis, Fluency, and Systematic Vocabulary Development

Name ______________________________

In both fiction and nonfiction stories, someone may face a **problem** and then find a **solution**, or a way to solve it.

Read the passage. Then answer the questions that follow.

Wangari Maathai is an African woman who wanted to help her people. She knew that the land of her country, Kenya, needed more care. She also knew that many Africans did not have enough food. She had an idea. She got women to start planting trees. Since 1976, the Green Belt movement has helped 80,000 women plant and care for more than 20 million trees! The environment has improved, and people now eat the bananas, mangoes, and papayas that grow on the trees.

Tree planting is not the only way Maathai has helped the environment. When plans were made to build a skyscraper in Nairobi's only park, she organized demonstrations against it and wrote letters to stop it. She was put in jail, but her letters and the public protests stopped the building from being built. For her work, Maathai has received many honors, including the Nobel Peace Prize.

1. Who is this passage about? ______________________

2. What is one problem Maathai faced?

____

3. What other problem did Maathai face?

____

4. What solution did she come up with?

____

Name ______________________________

As you read *How Ben Franklin Stole the Lightning*, fill in the Problem and Solution Chart.

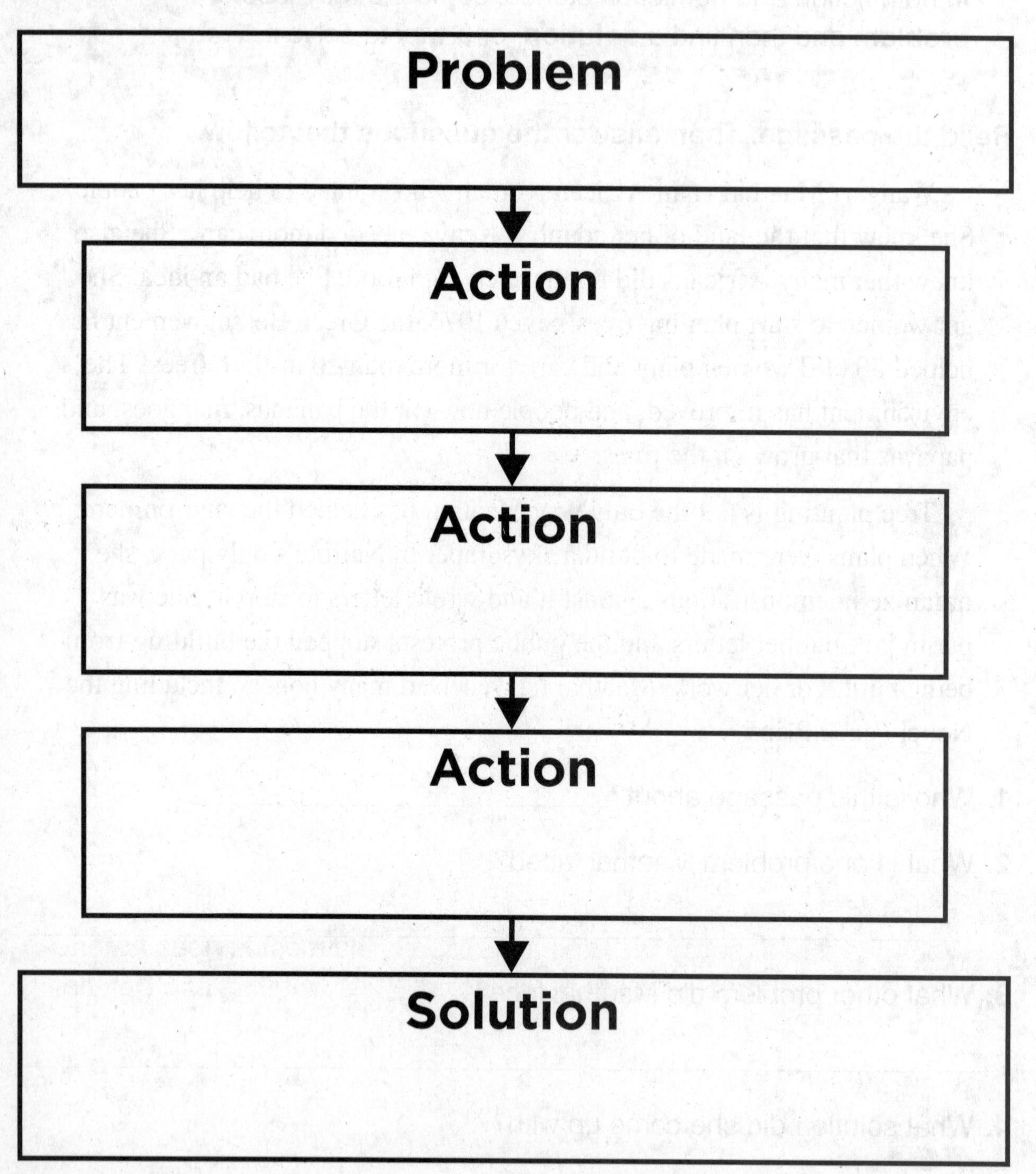

How does the information you wrote in the Problem and Solution Chart help you to generate questions about *How Ben Franklin Stole the Lightning*?

Name ____________________

As I read, I will pay attention to match my pacing with the energy of the passage.

	What would the world be like without light bulbs?
9	We have Thomas Edison to thank for that bright idea!
19	He also invented the phonograph and motion pictures.
27	Thomas Edison is the most famous American inventor.
35	He came up with more than 1,000 new devices. He worked
45	with electricity and technology to make our daily lives
54	better.
55	Find out how this one man changed history through his
65	inventions.
66	The 1800s have been called "The Age of Invention."
74	That is because many things were invented at that time.
84	It seemed like a whirlwind of inventions!
91	The first steamboat, steam-engine train, and airplane
98	were invented during this time. The telephone was invented
107	too. These inventions changed the way people lived and
116	worked. 117

Comprehension Check

1. How did Thomas Edison's inventions solve problems? **Problem and Solution**

2. When the author says that Thomas Edison is the most famous American inventor, is this statement a fact or opinion? **Relevant Fact and Details**

	Words Read	–	Number of Errors	=	Words Correct Score
First Read		–		=	
Second Read		–		=	

R 1.1 Read narrative and expository text aloud with grade-appropriate fluency and accuracy and with appropriate pacing, intonation, and expression.

Name ______________________________

Practice

Literary Element: Figurative Language and Alliteration

Figurative language, such as metaphors and similes, uses words in fresh ways to suggest vivid images.
Metaphor: Sam is a tower of strength.
Simile: That man was as strong as a horse!
Alliteration is the repetition of the same first letter or consonant sound in a series of words. It was **B**lake's **b**lue **b**lanket.

Read the poem. Then circle or fill in the correct answer.

The wonderful wheel, which changed the world,
Is as round as a ring and rolls and twirls
For carts and coaches,
Cabbies and kings.
The wonderful wheel—oh, what bustle it brings!

1. What is this poem about?
   a. a wheel　　**b.** a ring
2. Which words in the poem show alliteration?
   a. round, rolls, ring　　**b.** twirls and changed
3. Which is a simile?
   a. carts and coaches　　**b.** as round as a ring
4. A simile is a kind of ______.
   a. alliteration　　**b.** figurative language
5. What are the two reasons why "carts" was placed with "coaches" and "cabbies" was placed with "kings"? ______________________________

____

____

____

CA **R 3.5** Define figurative language (e.g., simile, metaphor, hyperbole, personification) and identify its use in literary works.

Name ______________________________

Idioms are words or groups of words that cannot be understood by figuring out the meaning of each word. Example: pulling my leg. This group of words means "to trick or to tease." You can use context clues to help you understand the meaning of an idiom.

1. Read the sentence; then circle the meaning of "out of the blue."

The news came *out of the blue*, so Isaac was shocked.

a. suddenly **b.** out of the sky

2. Use "out of the blue" in a sentence.

____

3. Read the sentence; then circle the meaning of "to wind up."

The meeting was almost over when Janet said, "Let's *wind up* by six o'clock."

a. change time on the clock **b.** finish

4. Use "wind up" in a sentence.

____

5. Read the sentence; then circle the meaning of "under the weather."

Zachary was rarely sick, so his teacher was surprised to hear that he was *under the weather.*

a. lying under a cloud **b.** feeling sick

6. Use "under the weather" in a sentence.

____

Name ______________________________

Practice

Spelling: Suffixes and Prefixes

Using the Word Study Steps

1. LOOK at the word.
2. SAY the word aloud.
3. STUDY the letters in the word.
4. WRITE the word.
5. CHECK the word.

   Did you spell the word right?
   If not, go back to step 1.

Add the Missing Vowels

Fill in the missing vowels to write a spelling word.

1. h ___ pp ___ l ___
2. ___ nch ___ ng ___ d
3. n ___ nf ___ ct ___ ___ n
4. ___ nt ___ rst ___ t ___
5. pr ___ j ___ dg ___
6. ___ v ___ rs ___ z ___ d
7. d ___ fl ___ t ___
8. r ___ st ___ t ___
9. ___ nfr ___ q ___ ___ nt
10. n ___ nst ___ p
11. d ___ s ___ pp ___ ___ nt
12. r ___ v ___ rs ___
13. s ___ m ___ w ___ ___ kl ___
14. ___ nn ___ m ___ d
15. f ___ ___ rf ___ l

LC 1.7 Spell correctly roots, inflections, suffixes and prefixes, and syllable constructions.

Name ______________________

A. Proofreading

There are six spelling mistakes in the story below. Circle the misspelled words. Write the words correctly on the lines below.

Becoming an inventor is not easy. For most inventors, the search for a new idea is nonnstop. Some inventors get ideas from reading nonficsion books. Others think about things that will make life easier for their family and friends.

Tim noticed that his mother carried an oversised purse. He invented a belt that had pouches for cups, snacks, keys, and money. His mom happiley helped him sew his design. The invention was unamed until Tim's sister said "Look, Mom has a tool belt." "Mom's Tool Belt" won an intrstate invention contest for young inventors. Tim was so excited!

1. ____________ **3.** ____________ **5.** ____________

2. ____________ **4.** ____________ **6.** ____________

B. Writing Activity

Write about an invention you would like to create. Use at least four spelling words in your paragraph.

____

____

____

____

CA LC 1.7 Spell correctly roots, inflections, suffixes and prefixes, and syllable constructions.

Name ______________________________

Two sentences can be combined by adding a **prepositional phrase** to one sentence.

Rewrite the pairs of sentences below, using the prepositional phrase to combine them into one sentence.

1. Ants make their anthills by digging. They dig through dirt.

____

2. Ants scoop dirt. They scoop with their jaws.

____

3. Ants live like people. They live in social communities.

____

4. Most ants live and work together. They live under the ground.

____

5. The queen ant lays eggs. She does this inside the hive.

____

6. Worker ants protect the queen. They protect her from harm.

____

7. Male ants die. They die after mating with the queen.

____

8. Ant eggs develop into adult ants. They develop after three months.

____

CA **LC 1.2** Combine short, related sentences with appositives, participial phrases, adjectives, adverbs, and prepositional phrases.

Name ______________________________

Read the passage below. Combine each pair of underlined sentences into one sentence by adding a prepositional phrase. Write the combination sentences on the lines below.

I read an interesting book. It was about ants. The book says that ants are one of the greatest insects around. Ants protect plants. They protect them from other insects. Also, they feed the dirt with good things so that we can grow pretty flowers, like Mr. Chang's pink roses! There are three kinds of ants that help each other. They help to get things done.

Worker ants look after the other ants. They do this by gathering food, watching the queen and her eggs, and building the anthill. Male ants don't live long, but they help the queen produce lots of eggs. Finally, there's the queen ant. She is the mother of all the ants. Without her, none of the ants would have anything to do! I recommend this book to all kids who want to learn more about ants and the way they live.

1. ______________________________

2. ______________________________

3. ______________________________

____

4. ______________________________

____

____

CA **LC 1.2** Combine short, related sentences with appositives, participial phrases, adjectives, adverbs, and prepositional phrases.

Name ____________________

Practice

Writing: Character Development: Change in Behavior of a Character

1. The best way to tell that someone has changed or grown is to look at how they act. Practice with an imaginary character. Here is a list of activities that a person might not like:
   - Getting new braces
   - Sleeping away from home
   - Getting a haircut
   - Going to the dentist
   - Eating mushrooms
2. Pick one of the items on the list and write it on the line. ____________
3. Write 2–3 sentences showing what your character did and said when he or she didn't like the thing you chose.

____

____

____

____

____

____

4. Write 2–3 sentences showing what your character does and says now that he or she does like the thing you chose.

____

____

____

____

____

____

____

CA W 1.0 Writing Strategies

Common noun	Proper noun
School	Podesta
Weak verb	Strong verb
Said	yelled
look	Peaked
fly	glide
get	achieve